Quizzes and Diagnostic Tests
to Accompany

RULES FOR WRITERS

Sixth Edition

Diana Hacker

Wanda Van Goor
Prince George's Community College

ESL test items by
MITCH EVICH
Northeastern University

BEDFORD/ST. MARTIN'S   BOSTON ◆ NEW YORK

Manufactured in the United States of America.

3   2   1   0   9   8
f   e   d   c   b   a

For information, write: Bedford/St. Martin's, 75 Arlington
Street, Boston, MA 02116 (617–399–4000)

ISBN-10: 0–312–47281–1
ISBN-13: 978–0–312–47281–8

Contents

Part One

QUIZZES

Quiz 8-1:   Active verbs

Edit the following sentences to make passive or weak *be* verbs active. All of the sentences need revision. Example:

~~We were hit broadside by~~ the student driver.
T   *broadsided us*

1. Two players were asked by the coach to visit local schools.

2. It was learned from the survey that our staff wanted more training.

3. Patients taking this medication are warned on the label not to drink alcohol.

4. More than one million dollars will be given to disaster survivors by CareAmerica.

5. For as long as I can remember, grace has been said before every meal at our house.

6. No courtesy at all was shown by the local police to the peaceful protesters.

7. It can be concluded that a college education provides a significant economic advantage.

8. Families with children are often denied housing by landlords who want to avoid making repairs.

9. Six complaints against the retail chain are under investigation by the commission.

10. The students were punished by the principal before they were given a chance to explain.

Quiz 9-1:   Parallelism

Edit the following sentences to correct faulty parallelism. Example:

                                                               complete

Susan wanted to earn a degree in business administration as well as ~~completing~~ the require-

ments for her secretarial certificate.

1. Ari helped by painting the fence, trimming shrubs, mulching flowerbeds, and leaf raking.

2. Sebastian liked playing video games more than to watch television.

3. The computer salesperson promised not only that I would receive a rebate but also a free iPod.

4. Rina was hired to stock merchandise, write orders for delivery, and sales of computers.

5. Michiko told the judge that she had been pulled out of a line of fast-moving traffic and of her perfect driving record.

6. To administer the poison, the tribe's sorcerers put it in their victims' food, throw it into their huts, or it can be dropped into their mouths or nostrils while they sleep.

7. Sylvia loved swimming, canoeing, and to hike.

8. Julius realized that he was a talented violinist but proper training and discipline would be the best foundation for a career as a musician.

9. Bill found that it was harder to be fair to himself than being fair to others.

10. At the arts-and-crafts table, the children make potholders, key rings, weave baskets, paint pictures, and assemble model cars.

Quiz 10-1:   Needed words

Add any words needed for grammatical or logical completeness in the following sentences. Example:

those of
Their starting salaries are higher than ʌ other professionals with more seniority.

1. As Luis began cooking, he noticed his friend's vintage 1950s oven wasn't working properly.

2. For many years Americans had trust and affection for Walter Cronkite.

3. Years of skateboarding made Jason's reflexes much sharper than his brother.

4. The study showed that tenth graders are more polite to strangers than ninth graders.

5. My adviser was someone whom I saw frequently on campus but never seemed to be in his office.

6. The cougar's eyeball, pupil, and lens are proportionately larger than other carnivores.

7. When the fishing trip was canceled, my dad was as disappointed, if not more disappointed than, his granddaughter.

8. Phyllis says that she never has registered to vote in the primaries and never will.

9. To patch a deep hole, work first coat of patching into place with putty knife, pressing in plaster.

10. Uncle Cecil's pies won far more prizes than Aunt Margaret.

Quiz 11-1:   Mixed constructions

Edit the following sentences to untangle mixed constructions. Example:

The ~~increase in the~~ Dow Jones Industrial average has been rising daily.

1. The astronomer, an ancient science, was especially important to agricultural societies.

2. By pushing the button for the insert mode opens the computer's CD-ROM drive.

3. When one is exposed to summer sun without protection can be dangerous.

4. The reason Frank burned the bread is because he was talking on the telephone.

5. Thailand has been transformed into one of the fastest growing stock exchanges in the world.

6. Floyd Fay failed a polygraph test and demanded a second one, in which he also failed.

7. Who would have thought that a department store salesperson could be a life-threatening job?

8. Seoul, Korea, is where you can get exceptional bargains — if you are prepared to negotiate.

9. The growth in the number of applications is increasing rapidly.

10. In the area near the victim's garage provided the investigators with several important clues.

Quiz 12-1: Misplaced and dangling modifiers

Edit the following sentences to correct misplaced or dangling modifiers. Example:

only
Sid ~~only~~ wanted to see ∧the end of the film again, not the full two hours.

1. He promised never to remarry at her deathbed.

2. In late 1973, the major oil producers put an embargo on crude oil sent to the United States that shocked the nation.

3. Although wearing only a diaper, the EMT reported that the rescued infant had no signs of hypothermia.

4. At the next train stop, all doors will not open. [*Some doors will open.*]

5. Señor Tejada is prepared to as soon as possible fly to Belize.

6. All passengers were, as the train reached the border, asked to have their passports ready.

7. After more than ten years of living on the streets, social workers persuaded Jason to take one of the new medications for schizophrenia.

8. This form is only required when the traveler is receiving an advance.

9. The fund is designed for those who want to quickly gain above-average returns.

10. Thinking that justice had finally prevailed, Lydia's troubles were just beginning.

Quiz 13-1:   Shifts

Edit the following sentences to correct distracting shifts. Example:

As I drove along Route 6, ~~you~~ *I* could see the many cars that had slid off the road.

1. A pilot flying in bad weather relies on their instruments for safe navigation.

2. On Saturday we cleaned the attic and discovered a bundle of love letters you knew would embarrass our parents.

3. Ming-Na told me she could convert my CDs to MP3 format and when could she come over to get started.

4. Our class visited a museum of living history, where we saw how people had lived in a nineteenth-century village. We participated in several activities. For example, you were shown how to spin and weave.

5. We always follow the same routine at the campground. First, we erected the tent, rolled out the sleeping bags, and set up the kitchen; then we all head for the swimming pool.

6. Police officers follow strict codes of safety. For example, always point the barrel of the gun upward when the gun is not in use.

7. Everyone should get to the stadium early unless you want to stand in line with mobs of people waiting for tickets.

8. We wondered whether the water was clean enough to drink and could we swim in it.

9. With a little self-discipline and a desire to improve oneself, you too can enjoy the benefits of running.

10. One tour guide collects the tickets and another will give out the maps.

Combine the following sentences by subordinating minor ideas or by coordinating ideas of equal importance. You must decide which ideas are minor because the sentences are given out of context. Example:

Stepping   *the senator*
~~The senator stepped~~ out of the airplane, ~~She~~ waved to the cheering students and thanked them for their support.

1. My grandmother left the house before I got home every Tuesday. She sang in the local jazz club.

2. His famous kite experiment was extremely dangerous. It gave Franklin important insights into the nature of electricity.

3. Anesh told her boss she would manage the project. The project was behind schedule. The project was also understaffed.

4. The Web site looked professional and was sponsored by an organization that sounded reputable. We soon realized that it was full of misinformation.

5. The human heart is well protected. It lies behind the breastbone, between the lungs, and above the diaphragm. The diaphragm is a tough layer of muscle.

6. My mother is trying to cut down on the fat in her diet. She doesn't use oil. She uses yogurt instead.

7. Every day Sisyphus helplessly repeated the same meaningless task. He pushed a heavy stone up a steep mountain. He then stepped aside and watched as it rolled back down again.

8. Their workhorse was used primarily for pulling the plow. Their daughter sometimes rode it through the woods to visit the neighbors.

9. The Web site offers summaries of articles. Those articles have appeared in the past three issues. The site charges for access to the full text of the articles.

10. Table tennis is also known as Ping-Pong. It became an Olympic sport in 1988. My brother was then inspired to begin practicing.

Quiz 19-1:   Sentence fragments

Repair any fragments by attaching them to nearby sentences or rewriting them as complete sentences. Do not change correct sentences. Example:

she
Though Katie hadn't finished the memo, ~~She~~ decided to go to lunch.
                                    ^

1. English has borrowed many words from Spanish. Such as *adobe, bravado,* and *mosquito.*

2. After my test drive, I came to a conclusion. That purchasing a hybrid vehicle was a smart move.

3. As we walked up the path, we came upon the gun barrels. Large gray concrete structures covered with ivy and weeds.

4. Standardized testing has produced a great deal of apprehension among elementary school teachers. So that many teachers, in fact, have considered petitioning the education department.

5. The horses were dressed up with hats and flowers. Some even wore sunglasses.

6. I felt caught between two worlds. The world of my friends in my urban neighborhood and the world of my suburban college campus.

7. Keiko arrived in the village of Futagami. Where she was to spend the summer with her grandparents.

8. I had pushed these fears into one of those quiet places in my mind. Hoping they would stay there asleep.

9. Aspiring bodybuilders must first determine their strengths and weaknesses. And then decide what they want to achieve.

10. The side effects of lithium are many. Nausea, stomach cramps, thirst, muscle weakness, vomiting, diarrhea, confusion, and tremors.

Quiz 20-1:   Run-on sentences

___

Revise each run-on sentence using a technique that you find effective. Do not change correct sentences. Example:

$$so$$
My class was canceled, ~~therefore,~~ I spent extra time in the writing center.
$$\wedge$$

1. Shoshana renewed her driver's license a day later she lost it.

2. The world of digital music is incredibly flexible, people can even download songs to a cell phone.

3. The Carrier Air Wing Eight, called CVW-8, is made up of ten squadrons, each with its own mission and role.

4. The suburbs seemed cold, they lacked the warmth and excitement of our Italian neighborhood.

5. Monument Beach was closed for the day, therefore we decided to see a movie.

6. Why should we pay taxes to support public transportation, we prefer to save energy by carpooling.

7. After days of struggling with her dilemma, Rosa came to a decision, she would sacrifice herself for her people and her cause.

8. While we were walking down Grover Avenue, Gary told us about his Aunt Elsinia, she was an extraordinary woman.

9. After the rain had stopped, we staked the outline of the path and broke the ground by late morning, then we tamped down the earth, laid the gravel, and set the bricks in place.

10. Paloma is an experienced guide she will answer any questions you might have about the history and geography of the region.

Edit the following sentences to eliminate problems with subject-verb agreement. Do not change correct sentences. Example:

have
Chiyo's friendly manner and good sense ~~has~~ made the transaction go smoothly.
                                    ∧

1. The peeling paint and the broken railing makes our home appear older than its twenty years.

2. Moldy tomatoes in the refrigerator are not a pretty sight.

3. The most significant lifesaving device in automobiles are air bags.

4. There is several cups of tea on the table.

5. Our express mail costs this past year have risen 25 percent.

6. Only one of the many architectural treatises written in antiquity survive.

7. Every year a number of kokanee salmon, not native to the region, is introduced into Flathead Lake.

8. The angry crowd was now surging over the bridge.

9. Neither Lateef nor Samuel usually works on Fridays.

10. At MGM Studios at Disney World, the wonders of moviemaking comes alive.

Edit the following sentences to eliminate problems with pronoun-antecedent agreement. Avoid using sexist pronouns, and where possible revise the sentence without using the wordy constructions *he or she* and *his or her.* Do not change correct sentences. Example:

> *to*
> **Each player must decide which card ~~they will~~ play first.**
>   ∧

1. The group was expected to travel as a unit and make their plans by consensus.

2. When the client comes to the writing center, they should feel comfortable enough to seek advice.

3. The National Organization for Women was founded in 1966. That same year, they fought sex discrimination in the airline industry.

4. Irina gave the book to someone who lent it to their relative.

5. If anybody wishes to pay by check, they should see the manager for approval.

6. No one should be forced to sacrifice their prized possession — life — for someone else.

7. The board of directors was unanimous in their decision to offer health benefits to part-time workers.

8. A good teacher is patient with his or her students, and they maintain an even temper.

9. By the final curtain, 90 percent of the audience had voted with their feet.

10. On the first day of class, Mr. Bhatti asked each student why they wanted to stop smoking.

Edit the following sentences to correct errors in pronoun reference. In some cases you may need to decide on an antecedent that the pronoun might logically refer to. Example:

the fog
The sky was still gray, but we thought ~~it~~ would burn off.
^

1. In Jodi Picoult's novel *My Sister's Keeper,* she explores medical ethics.

2. If you have a sweet tooth, visit the confectioner's shop, where it is still made as it was a hundred years ago.

3. The Registry of Motor Vehicles is more user-friendly now. They even allow individuals to renew licenses online.

4. After working in the apple orchard all morning, we took a bushel of them home to eat.

5. He recognized her as the woman that had won an Olympic gold medal for swimming.

6. Juan told Jeremy that he had been promoted.

7. In John Donne's poetry, he often juxtaposes the sacred with the profane.

8. In Saudi Arabia it is considered ill mannered for you to reject a gift.

9. When Tia Elena put the cake on the table, it collapsed.

10. Be sure to visit Istanbul's bazaar, where they sell everything from Persian rugs to electronic calculators.

Edit the following sentences to eliminate errors in case. Do not change correct sentences. Example:

No one could be more surprised by the award than ~~me.~~ *I.*

1. Professor Gerroir gave Marlo and I the opportunity to conduct field research.

2. Two fortunate art students, Jonas Jurgis and I, are going to design a new home page for the art department.

3. Jasmine can't come to the party because her and her brother will be out of town that day.

4. I am jealous that our dog likes my neighbor more than I.

5. Doctors should take more seriously what us patients say about our treatment.

6. Randy came with my grandfather and I to the baseball game.

7. I was nine when my uncle and I last saw each other.

8. It is strange how people in other countries often seem much happier than us.

9. I am sure that we will all be scolded for John laughing during the most solemn moment of the ceremony.

10. My older sister promised to leave her old laptop behind for Paulette and I.

Edit the following sentences to eliminate errors in the use of *who* and *whom*. Do not change correct sentences. Example:

                                                       whom

    Shima had seen so many good candidates for the job that she didn't know ~~who~~ to believe.

1. I hope you like Kendra, whom is also coming to lunch.

2. For whom did you vote in the city elections?

3. They will become business partners with whomever is willing to contribute to the company's coffers.

4. My mother never knew that she learned Italian from a man who was Russian.

5. The elderly woman who I was asked to take care of was a clever, delightful companion.

6. Some group leaders cannot handle the pressure; they give whomever makes the most noise most of their attention.

7. Who did the commission appoint?

8. "In that costume they will never realize whom you are!" laughed the duke.

9. I was very excited about meeting Serena Williams, who I had admired all my life.

10. The young man who I danced with was an exchange student from Italy.

Edit the following sentences to eliminate problems with irregular verbs. Do not change correct sentences. Example:

> *saw*
> Was it you I ~~seen~~ last night at the concert?
> ^

1. Frustrated that no one responded to my knocking, I rung the doorbell three times.

2. Last weekend Sanya swum the 50-meter backstroke in 32 seconds.

3. Laying on the operating table, I could hear only the beating of my heart.

4. In just a week the ground had froze, and the first winter storm had left over a foot of snow.

5. Jet lag must have caught up with me; I lay down for a nap yesterday afternoon — and woke up this morning.

6. When the career counselor gave interviewing tips, Scott clinged to her words as if they were gold.

7. The editor explained that the designer had shrank the image to fit the layout.

8. After seeing her dance in the musical, I would have swore that she was professionally trained.

9. No matter how much lemonade the budding entrepreneur made, she knew it would be drank.

10. The koala had sprung from its cage the day before we visited the zoo.

Add or delete commas where necessary in the following sentences. Do not change correct sentences. Example:

> **The Scott Pack, which is a twenty-five-pound steel bottle of air, is designed to be worn on a**
>   **∧**   **∧**
> **firefighter's back.**

1. As I was finishing an entry in my blog my supervisor appeared at my office door.

2. The speaker approached the podium with casual elegant grace.

3. Owning a home which is a dream for many Americans seems out of reach when interest rates soar.

4. The study participants began the behavioral therapy, and saw immediate results.

5. The lawyer fully explained the contract, but we weren't certain we understood all of its implications.

6. Cobbled streets too narrow for two cars to pass, were lined with tiny houses leaning so close together they almost touched.

7. Armed with a tape recorder, notepad, and camera, I interviewed residents of Laura, Ohio, where my grandmother's family lived during the Depression.

8. In one corner of the attic, was a box of letters written in the late eighteenth century.

9. Tim O'Brien's third novel *Going After Cacciato* won the National Book Award.

10. It has been reported that the Republican who suggested Eisenhower as a presidential candidate meant Milton not Ike.

Edit the following sentences to correct errors in the use of the semicolon and the comma. Do not change correct sentences. Example:

;
Butter will not ease the pain of a burn or improve healing/in fact, butter traps heat and moisture in the skin.

1. The Anglo-American row house achieved its definitive form in seventeenth-century London and was the product of specific social conditions, above all, it was created to meet the needs of an increasingly affluent middle class.

2. Before Chao Neng started his internship; he had no idea how much writing engineers do on the job.

3. It is one thing to be able to read a foreign language with ease, it is quite another to speak it fluently.

4. The hills above the city were deforested, so eroded soil washed into the rivers and silted up the city's harbors.

5. Many people believe that bats are vicious, in fact, bats are helpful because they eat mosquitoes in large numbers.

6. To my companions, the painting's technique transcended the subject matter, to me it was nothing more than a painting of an old shoe.

7. Culinary experts tend to frown on microwave cooking; which hardens bread and turns the tenderest cuts of meat to rubber.

8. We knew that the river road might be flooded, therefore, we decided to take the longer route through the mountains.

9. DeafREACH runs a group home, which prepares residents to live independently; a daytime activity center, where walk-in clients receive job training; and a community service center, which provides counseling and legal representation.

10. The twentieth century saw a bewildering succession of popular dance styles; such as the Charleston, the tango, the jitterbug, the twist, the frug, and break dancing.

Edit the following sentences to correct errors in the use of the colon, the semicolon, and the comma. Do not change correct sentences. Example:

One saying of my mother's has stayed with me for years: "You're only as good as your feet."

1. Ireland has produced an extraordinary number of major literary figures; Oscar Wilde, William Butler Yeats, and James Joyce, to name a few.

2. A flower's reproductive organs consist of: the ovary, the style, the stigma, and the stamen.

3. The Benelux is a European economic union composed of three countries: Belgium, the Netherlands, and Luxembourg.

4. The bomb had torn apart the building and scattered a strange assortment of objects across the street; a television, a dining room set, and several mannequins.

5. Among the classes being offered were: Web design, art history, and French.

6. In his introduction to Katharine White's book on gardening, E. B. White describes his wife's writing process: "The editor in her fought the writer every inch of the way; the struggle was felt all through the house. She would write eight or ten words, then draw her gun and shoot them down."

7. He gazed with dread at the dark shape on the horizon: a tornado!

8. The second and most memorable week of survival school consisted of five stages; orientation, long treks, POW camp, escape and evasion, and return to civilization.

9. Every camper should consider carrying the following items, a first-aid kit, a Swiss army knife, and a flashlight.

10. Hans decided to enrich his life with new cultural activities, such as: visiting the modern art museum, taking Chinese lessons, and learning to use a darkroom.

Underline the nouns and circle any noun/adjectives in the following sentences. Example:

He is in the(dog)house.

1. Convictions are more dangerous enemies of truth than lies.   — Friedrich Nietzsche

2. Today's shocks are tomorrow's conventions.   — Carolyn Heilbrun

3. Proper words in proper places make the true definition of style.   — Jonathan Swift

4. A man must come into a court of equity with clean hands.   — Legal maxim

5. Necessity is the mother of invention.   — Jonathan Swift

6. In the Chinese family system, there is superficial quiet and calmness and quarreling is

    frowned upon, but in reality all is in conflict.   — Ting Ling

7. Advice after injury is like medicine after death.   — Danish proverb

8. The children are always the chief victims of social chaos.   — Agnes Myer

9. An iron curtain has descended across the continent.   — Winston Churchill

10. Frankness is usually a euphemism for rudeness.   — Muriel Spark

Quiz 62-2: Identifying pronouns

Underline the pronouns and circle any pronoun/adjectives in the following sentences. Example:

The louder <u>he</u> talked of (his) honor, the faster <u>we</u> counted (our) spoons.

1. One cannot collect all the beautiful shells on the beach. — Anne Morrow Lindbergh

2. Never allow your child to call you by your first name. He hasn't known you long enough.

— Fran Lebowitz

3. She ransacked her mind but there was nothing in it. — Joyce Carol Oates

4. Those who aim low usually hit their target. — Proverb

5. The man [or woman] who makes no mistakes usually does not make anything.

— Bishop W. C. Magee

6. Do not deprive me of my age. I have earned it. — May Sarton

7. We want to live long, but none of us wants to grow old. — Anonymous

8. Do not needlessly endanger your lives until I give you the signal.

— Dwight D. Eisenhower

9. She gave me a look that you could have poured on a waffle. — Ring Lardner

10. When you come to a fork in a road, take it. — Yogi Berra

In each of the following sentences, underline the verb or verbs (main verbs and any helping verbs). Remember that adverbs are not part of the verb. Example:

Rain <u>does</u> not <u>fall</u> on only one roof.

1. Every artist should be allowed a few failures.   — Elsa Lanchester

2. Power should not be concentrated in the hands of so few, and powerlessness in the hands of so many.   — Maggie Khun

3. The gardens of kindness never fade.   — Greek proverb

4. The life of the law has not been logic; it has been experience.

     — Oliver Wendell Holmes Jr.

5. Memory is the mother of all wisdom.   — Aeschylus

6. We are drowning in information and starving for knowledge.   — Rutherford D. Rogers

7. The faultfinder will find faults even in paradise.   — Thoreau

8. Seek simplicity and distrust it.   — Alfred North Whitehead

9. Advertising has annihilated the power of the most powerful adjectives.   — Paul Valéry

10. Life can only be understood backwards, but it must be lived forwards.

     — Søren Kierkegaard

Quiz 62-4: Identifying adjectives and adverbs

Underline the adjectives and circle the adverbs in the following sentences. If a word is a noun or a pronoun in form but an adjective in function, treat it as an adjective. (Do not underline the articles *a, an,* and *the.*) Example:

A spoiled child never loves its mother.

1. Fat hens lay few eggs. — German proverb

2. Never underestimate the power of the irate customer.

— Joel E. Ross and Michael J. Kami

3. Democracy is not a spectator sport. — Marian Wright Edelman

4. Success and failure are equally disastrous. — Tennessee Williams

5. A small leak will sink a great ship. — English proverb

6. Horses are predictably unpredictable. — Loretta Gage

7. If you command wisely, you will be obeyed cheerfully. — Thomas Fuller

8. Kindness is always fashionable. — Amelia E. Barr

9. The little stations are very proud because the expresses must pass them by.

— Karl Kraus

10. If you keep your mind sufficiently open, people will throw a lot of rubbish into it.

— William A. Orton

Identify the part of speech of each underlined word. Above the word, write ADJ (for adjective), ADV (for adverb), C (for conjunction), N (for noun), P (for preposition), PN (for pronoun), or V (for verb). Example:

         ADV   *ADV*
   If the sailors become <u>too</u> <u>numerous</u>, the ship sinks.

1. Men <u>often</u> applaud the imitation and hiss the <u>real</u> thing.   — Aesop

2. Agreement is made more <u>precious</u> by <u>disagreement.</u>   — Publilius Syrus

3. Victory <u>has</u> a hundred fathers, <u>but</u> defeat is an orphan.   — Count Galeazzo Ciano

4. Only dead fish swim <u>with</u> the <u>stream.</u>   — Linda Ellerbee

5. He leaped <u>from</u> the frying pan <u>into</u> the fire.   — English proverb

6. The raft of knowledge <u>ferries</u> the worst sinners to <u>safety.</u>   — Bhagavad Gita

7. If <u>you</u> rest, you <u>rust.</u>   — Helen Hayes

8. Innovators are <u>inevitably</u> <u>controversial.</u>   — Eva Le Gallienne

9. The <u>loftiest</u> towers always <u>rise</u> from the ground.   — Chinese proverb

10. <u>Facts</u> speak for <u>themselves.</u>   — Terence

Underline all complete subjects and put SS above each simple subject. If the subject is an understood "you," insert the word in brackets: [You]. Example:

> *SS*
> **One bag of money is stronger than two bags of truth.**

1. Our capacity for justice makes democracy possible, but our inclination to injustice

   makes democracy necessary.   — Reinhold Niebuhr

2. In the eyes of a lover, pockmarks are dimples.   — Japanese proverb

3. In golden pots are hidden the most deadly poisons.   — Thomas Draxe

4. Never go to bed mad; stay up and fight.   — Phyllis Diller

5. The heresy of one age becomes the orthodoxy of the next.   — Helen Keller

6. A trout in the pot is better than a salmon in the sea.   — Irish proverb

7. Anger and worry are the enemies of clear thought.   — Madeleine Brent

8. The greatest right in the world is the right to be wrong.   — Harry Weinberger

9. Keep your mouth shut and your eyes open.   — Samuel Palmer

10. The frog in the well knows nothing of the ocean.   — Proverb

Label the direct objects and subject complements DO or SC in the following sentences. If a direct object or subject complement consists of more than one word, bracket and label all of it. Example:

$$SC$$
The best mirror is [an old friend].

1. The loftiest edifices need the deepest foundations.   — George Santayana

2. All extremes are dangerous.   — Virginia Woolf

3. A glutton digs his grave with his teeth.   — French proverb

4. History is a bucket of ashes.   — Carl Sandburg

5. You cannot put the same shoe on every foot.   — Publilius Syrus

6. You can prove anything with statistics.   — Proverb

7. Numbers constitute the only universal language.   — Nathanael West

8. Silence is one of the great arts of conversation.   — Hannah More

9. A sleeping fox counts hens in his dreams.   — Russian proverb

10. Congress seems drugged and inert most of the time.   — Shirley Chisholm

Quiz 63-3: Identifying objects and complements

Label any objects or complements SC (subject complement), DO (direct object), IO (indirect object), or OC (object complement). If an object or a complement consists of more than one word, bracket and label all of it. Example:

Most of us find [our own life histories]**SC** interesting.**OC**

1. Give me liberty or give me death.   — Patrick Henry

2. Every natural action is graceful.   — Ralph Waldo Emerson

3. A borrowed cloak does not keep one warm.   — Arab proverb

4. You cannot plan the future by the past.   — Proverb

5. Blues are the songs of despair, but gospel songs are the songs of hope.

                                                                 — Mahalia Jackson

6. Show me a happy camper, and I will show you an RV with all the comforts of home.

                                                                 — Anonymous

7. One misfortune carries another on its back.   — Dutch proverb

8. Revenge does not long remain unavenged.   — German proverb

9. Some folk want their luck buttered.   — Thomas Hardy

10. Racism is the snobbery of the poor.   — Raymond Aron

Quiz 64-1: Identifying prepositional phrases

Underline the prepositional phrases in the following sentences. Some sentences contain more than one prepositional phrase. Example:

The words <u>of a silent man</u> are never brought <u>to court.</u>

1. Throw a cat over a house, and it will land on its feet.   — English proverb

2. Without lies, humanity would perish of despair and boredom.   — Anatole France

3. Acceptance of prevailing standards often means [that] we have no standards of our own.   — Jean Toomer

4. Lying is done with words and also with silence.   — Adrienne Rich

5. War is the unfolding of miscalculations.   — Barbara Tuchman

6. God enters by a private door into every individual.   — Ralph Waldo Emerson

7. In youth, we learn; in age, we understand.   — Marie von Ebner-Eschenbach

8. Nothing comes from nothing.   — Lucretius

9. Wall Street begins in a river and ends in a graveyard.   — Anonymous

10. All generalizations are false, including this one.   — Alexander Chase

Quiz 64-1: Identifying prepositional phrases   **31**

Quiz 64-2:   Identifying subordinate clauses

Underline the subordinate clauses in the following sentences. A sentence may contain more than one subordinate clause. Example:

When people talk about the weather, I always feel that they mean something else.

1. You won't skid if you stay in a rut.   — Frank McKinney Hubbard

2. When people are least sure, they are often most dogmatic. — John Kenneth Galbraith

3. Psychiatry's chief contribution is that the toilet is the seat of the soul.

                                                            — Alexander Chase

4. Any party which takes credit for the rain must not be surprised if its opponents blame

    it for the drought.   — Dwight W. Morrow

5. People hate what they do not understand.   — Eva Le Gallienne

6. Although ambition by itself is a vice, it is often the parent of virtues.   — Quintillian

7. If you pull out a gray hair, seven will come to its funeral.

                                                            — Pennsylvania German proverb

8. People seldom read a book that is given to them.   — Samuel Johnson

9. An actor is a sculptor who carves in snow.   — Edwin Booth

10. What is asserted by a man is opinion; what is asserted by a woman is opinionated.

                                                            — Marya Mannes

Underline the verbal phrases in the following sentences. A sentence may contain more than one verbal phrase. Example:

    I call that <u>taking candy from a baby</u>.

1. Bearing the misfortunes of others is easy.   — Proverb

2. It is human nature to think wisely and to act foolishly.   — Anatole France

3. The ass loaded with gold still eats thistles.   — German proverb

4. To forget one's ancestors is to be a tree without roots.   — Chinese proverb

5. A man convinced against his will is not convinced.   — Laurence J. Peter

6. The best way to see divine light is to put out your own candle.   — Thomas Fuller

7. Three people united against a town can ruin it.   — Proverb

8. Logic is often used for defending our prejudices.   — Anonymous

9. In the United States, we have a society pervaded from top to bottom by contempt for the law.   — Barbara Tuchman

10. Beware of Greeks bearing gifts.   — Proverb

Quiz 65-1: Identifying sentence types

___

In each blank label the sentence type with one of the following abbreviations: S (simple), C (compound), CX (complex), or C-CX (compound-complex). Example:

__CX__ When you shoot an arrow of truth, dip its point in honey.

1. Where law ends, tyranny begins. — William Pitt the Elder

2. A single arrow is easily broken, but you can't break a bundle of ten.

— Japanese proverb

3. Empty barrels make the most noise. — English proverb

4. If you were born lucky, even your rooster will lay eggs. — Russian proverb

5. No one really listens to anyone else, and if you try it for a while, you'll see why.

— Mingon McLaughlin

6. A minority may be right; a majority is always wrong. — Henrik Ibsen

7. My books are friends that never fail me. — Thomas Carlyle

8. Children are made readers on the laps of their parents. — Emilie Buchwald

9. Dogs come when they're called; cats take a message and get back to you.

— Missy Dizick and Mary Bly

10. A ship in port is safe, but that is not what ships are built for. — Benazir Bhutto

Part Two

INTRODUCTION TO DIAGNOSTIC TESTS

The diagnostic tests in this manual are designed to be used with *Rules for Writers*, Sixth Edition. Forms A and B contain the same kinds of constructions in the same kinds of sentences. Either form may be used as a diagnostic tool at the beginning of the semester or as a competency check later. This package also comes with a set of tests for classrooms that include students from ESL (English as a second language) backgrounds. In the AA and BB versions, about a quarter of the items test points of grammar and usage that are particularly troublesome to nonnative speakers of English. The rest of the test items in the AA/BB versions are exactly the same as in forms A and B. (See the chart on p. 68.)

You might use the tests to diagnose problem areas for individual students and to help in designing individual programs of self-study. Or you might choose instead to diagnose the needs of a class as a whole to guide you in planning the semester.

CONTENT OF FORMS A AND B

The tests in forms A and B cover common student problems with sentence construction, grammar, and punctuation. Included are the following specific topics, listed in the order in which they appear in *Rules for Writers*, Sixth Edition. The distribution of the sixty test items appears in the column to the right.

SECTION IN *RULES FOR WRITERS*	TEST ITEMS
9 Parallelism	10, 45, 50
11 Mixed constructions	43, 53, 55
12 Misplaced and dangling modifiers	37, 44, 56, 59
13 Shifts	15, 19, 51
19 Sentence fragments	2, 16, 18, 38, 52
20 Run-on sentences	12, 17, 27, 47, 49
21 Subject-verb agreement	4, 22, 23, 28, 40, 54
22 Pronoun-antecedent agreement	5, 20, 35, 42
23 Pronoun reference	24
24 Pronoun case	6, 30, 41
25 Case of *who/whom*	33
26 Adjectives and adverbs	7, 9, 21

SECTION IN *RULES FOR WRITERS*	TEST ITEMS
27 Verb forms	8, 26, 31, 34, 60
27 Verb tense	3
32 The comma	1, 11, 29, 46, 57
33 Unnecessary commas	32, 36, 58
34 The semicolon	48
35 The colon	13
36 The apostrophe	14, 25, 39

Students' skills are tested in two ways. In Part One (35 items), students need only to recognize the error. In Part Two (25 items), students must decide which of four possible versions best states an idea.

CONTENT OF FORMS AA AND BB (with some ESL items)

In addition to the common student problems covered in the regular versions of the diagnostic tests (sentence construction, grammar, and punctuation), forms AA and BB each include sixteen items on common ESL problems.

SECTION IN *RULES FOR WRITERS*	TEST ITEMS
9 Parallelism	10, 45
11 Mixed constructions	43, 53, 55
12 Misplaced and dangling modifiers	37, 56, 59
13 Shifts	15, 19, 51
19 Sentence fragments	2, 18, 52
20 Run-on sentences	17, 27, 47
21 Subject-verb agreement	4, 23, 28, 40, 54
22 Pronoun-antecedent agreement	5, 20, 35, 42
24 Pronoun case	6, 41
26 Adjectives and adverbs	9, 21
27 Verb forms	8, 31, 34, 60
27 Verb tense	3
28 Problems with verbs (ESL)	1, 12, 16, 22, 24, 30, 32
29 Articles (ESL)	7, 26, 33, 50
30 Sentence structure (ESL)	29, 38, 44, 49, 58
32 The comma	11, 46, 57
33 Unnecessary commas	36
34 The semicolon	48
35 The colon	13
36 The apostrophe	14, 25, 39

Students' skills are tested in two ways. In Part One (35 items), students need only to recognize the error. In Part Two (25 items), students must decide which of four possible versions best states an idea.

ADMINISTERING THE TESTS

Each test requires forty-five minutes, plus an additional five minutes for distributing materials, giving instructions, and collecting materials.

To administer the test, you need these items:

1. Tests (copied from the masters in this manual).
2. Answer forms. If the tests are to be machine scored, use cards compatible with your school's equipment. The cards must have at least four options (A, B, C, D), and they must have space for sixty answers. If the tests are to be hand scored, photocopy the answer sheet on page 41 of this booklet.
3. Pencils or markers. For machine scoring, No. 2 pencils are ordinarily required, but some scanners call for special markers. Check with the testing personnel at your school.

When students are ready, distribute the answer forms, pencils, and tests. Ask students to put their names on the answer forms. The instructions on the tests are self-explanatory, but you may want to go over them briefly and ask if students have any questions. If the tests are to be machine scored, it's a good idea to remind students to darken their answers.

At the end of the period, before collecting the answer forms, tests, and pencils, you may want to remind students to erase any stray pencil markings on the answer forms and to make sure that their answers are sufficiently dark to be read by a machine.

SCORING THE TESTS

The answer key on page 97 is the same for forms A, B, AA, and BB. An answer template is provided at the end of this book. Simply lay the template over the student's sheet and mark each empty hole with a pen or other highlighter.

For machine scoring, deliver the answer forms to your testing center. If your school's machine has the capability, you may be able to request two different printouts: one showing each student's problem areas, the other showing problem areas for the class as a whole.

INTERPRETING THE TESTS

These diagnostic tests are not intended for placement purposes. Rather, they have been designed to be used by individual instructors as a quick diagnosis of the grammar and punctuation problems their students are likely to encounter when writing. An initial diagnosis will be confirmed (or, occasionally, not confirmed) once the students begin writing.

If you are using the test results to design individualized programs of self-study, the lists on pages 36–37 will show you which sections of *Rules for Writers*, Sixth Edition, the student should turn to. The list on page 36 covers forms A and B, and the list on page 37 covers forms AA and BB.

Part Three

DIAGNOSTIC TEST FORMS A AND B

FOR INSTRUCTORS: TOPICS TESTED IN
FORMS A AND B

Test Item	Topic Tested	Section in *Rules for Writers*	Test Item	Topic Tested	Section in *Rules for Writers*
1	Comma	32	31	Verbs: *lie/lay*	27
2	Sentence fragment	19	32	Comma (misuse of)	33
3	Verb tense	27	33	Case of *who/whom*	25
4	Subject-verb agreement	21	34	*-ed* ending	27
5	Pronoun-antecedent agreement	22	35	Pronoun-antecedent agreement	22
6	Pronoun case	24	36	Comma (misuse of)	33
7	Adjectives and adverbs	26	37	Dangling modifier	12
8	Verbs: irregular	27	38	Sentence fragment	19
9	Double negative	26	39	Apostrophe	36
10	Parallelism	9	40	Subject-verb agreement	21
11	Comma	32	41	Pronoun case	24
12	Run-on sentence	20	42	Pronoun-antecedent agreement	22
13	Colon (misuse of)	35	43	Mixed construction	11
14	Apostrophe	36	44	Misplaced modifier	12
15	Shift	13	45	Parallelism	9
16	Sentence fragment	19	46	Comma	32
17	Run-on sentence	20	47	Run-on sentence	20
18	Sentence fragment	19	48	Semicolon	34
19	Shift	13	49	Run-on sentence	20
20	Pronoun-antecedent agreement	22	50	Parallelism	9
21	Adjectives and adverbs	26	51	Shift	13
22	Subject-verb agreement	21	52	Sentence fragment	19
23	Subject-verb agreement	21	53	Mixed construction	11
24	Pronoun reference	23	54	Subject-verb agreement	21
25	Apostrophe	36	55	Mixed construction	11
26	Verbs: irregular	27	56	Misplaced modifier	12
27	Run-on sentence	20	57	Comma	32
28	Subject-verb agreement	21	58	Comma (misuse of)	33
29	Comma	32	59	Dangling modifier	12
30	Pronoun case	24	60	Verbs: irregular	27

Name _____ Section _____ Date _____

Instructor _____ Form _____

Instructions
1. Use only a No. 2 pencil.
2. Make a dark mark that completely fills the circle.
3. Erase cleanly.
4. Make no stray marks.

PART ONE   ## PART TWO

	A	B	C	D
1	○	○	○	○
2	○	○	○	○
3	○	○	○	○
4	○	○	○	○
5	○	○	○	○
6	○	○	○	○
7	○	○	○	○
8	○	○	○	○
9	○	○	○	○
10	○	○	○	○
11	○	○	○	○
12	○	○	○	○
13	○	○	○	○
14	○	○	○	○
15	○	○	○	○
16	○	○	○	○
17	○	○	○	○
18	○	○	○	○
19	○	○	○	○
20	○	○	○	○
21	○	○	○	○
22	○	○	○	○
23	○	○	○	○
24	○	○	○	○
25	○	○	○	○
26	○	○	○	○
27	○	○	○	○
28	○	○	○	○
29	○	○	○	○
30	○	○	○	○
31	○	○	○	○
32	○	○	○	○
33	○	○	○	○
34	○	○	○	○
35	○	○	○	○
36	○	○	○	○
37	○	○	○	○
38	○	○	○	○
39	○	○	○	○
40	○	○	○	○
41	○	○	○	○
42	○	○	○	○
43	○	○	○	○
44	○	○	○	○
45	○	○	○	○
46	○	○	○	○
47	○	○	○	○
48	○	○	○	○
49	○	○	○	○
50	○	○	○	○
51	○	○	○	○
52	○	○	○	○
53	○	○	○	○
54	○	○	○	○
55	○	○	○	○
56	○	○	○	○
57	○	○	○	○
58	○	○	○	○
59	○	○	○	○
60	○	○	○	○

DIAGNOSTIC TEST
FORM A

This test of English skills has two parts. When you finish Part One, go directly to Part Two. You have forty-five minutes to respond to sixty items, so you should not spend too much time on any one item.

Each item has four possible answers. Choose the best answer and mark the appropriate space on your answer form, making sure to blacken the space thoroughly and to erase any stray pencil markings.

PART ONE

This part of the test has thirty-five sentences. Some of them are correct; others have errors in grammar or punctuation. No sentence has more than one error.

Each sentence has four underlined segments lettered A, B, C, and D. Read the sentence carefully. If there is a grammar or punctuation error in any of the underlined parts of the sentence, blacken the space that corresponds to the letter under the underlined segment. If there is no error, blacken the D space on your answer form.

EXAMPLE:

Salmon always return to their birthplace at egg-laying time. Strong currents
                              A

and high waterfalls in a river does not keep them from swimming upstream
                                    B

to lay their eggs in that spot. No error.
 C   **D**

Answer: A   B   C   D

                    ○   ●   ○   ○

---

1. Because Paula wanted to study popular <u>astrology, not</u> classical <u>astronomy, she</u> was
   A   B
   told to apply to the community services <u>area not</u> the academic area. <u>No error.</u>
   C   D

2. The trainee for the <u>teller's position</u> was worried about his <u>speed and</u> unsure of his
   A   B
   computer <u>skills. Until</u> he learned the new system. <u>No error.</u>
   C   D

3. After Antigone <u>had buried</u> her brother, she was <u>brought</u> to the court and
   A   B
   <u>questioned</u> by the king. <u>No error.</u>
   C   D

4. Philip, unlike the thousands of students who <u>live</u> on campus, <u>has</u> to drive thirty
   A   B
   miles each day <u>to reach</u> the university. <u>No error.</u>
   C   D

5. The <u>modern American</u> family differs <u>in many significant</u> ways from <u>their</u>
   A   B   C
   nineteenth-century counterpart. <u>No error.</u>
   D

6. <u>It's</u> true that Sophie and <u>her</u> told Mark about the party, but <u>he</u> told the others.
   A   B   C
   <u>No error.</u>
   D

7. <u>Frantic,</u> Hal dialed the emergency phone number while Sarah tried <u>repeatedly</u>
   A   B
   to stop the bleeding; the rescue squad responded <u>quick</u> to the call for help.
   C

   <u>No error.</u>
   D

8. Young Ben <u>swore</u> he would not cry as his father <u>drug</u> the nearly dead sheepdog
   A   B
   toward the barn; Ben <u>clung</u> to the dog's fur, trying to help. <u>No error.</u>
   C   D

9. When the <u>disc jockey announced</u> the <u>winner's name</u>, Andrew <u>couldn't hardly</u> believe
   A   B   C
   his ears. <u>No error.</u>
   D

10. Pablo <u>said that</u> sports <u>had taught him</u> to follow instructions, to prepare
          A   **B**

    for games, to adjust to new situations, and <u>the value of losing as well as winning.</u>
                                                          C

    <u>No error.</u>
     D

11. The seventeen-year locusts <u>have descended</u> on <u>our town and</u> their noise actually
                               A   **B**

    <u>drowns</u> out my daughter's music. <u>No error.</u>
     C   **D**

12. The <u>young naval</u> officer in command had no control over the <u>accident that</u> killed
       A   **B**

    one of his <u>men, nevertheless,</u> the officer was held responsible for the death.
              C

    <u>No error.</u>
     D

13. Within the first thirty years of owning a <u>house, home owners</u> can count on having
                                        A

    <u>to: replace</u> several major appliances, put on a new roof, contract for termite
     B

    <u>treatment, and</u> pay about a third of their income each year for the privilege of dealing
       C

    with all these problems. <u>No error.</u>
                       D

14. The <u>poets remark</u> about the longevity of <u>things of beauty did</u> not take into account
        A   **B**

    the <u>effects of</u> such phenomena as acid rain. <u>No error.</u>
       C   **D**

15. Drivers should first fasten <u>their</u> seat belts. Next <u>they should</u> put the key all the way
                         A   **B**

    into the ignition. Then <u>you turn</u> the key to the right. <u>No error.</u>
                  C   **D**

16. The <u>paramedics,</u> who had been called <u>immediately, arrived</u> on the scene very
       A   **B**

    <u>quickly. And</u> knew exactly what to do. <u>No error.</u>
      C   **D**

17. We celebrated the Fourth of July with special fervor that <u>year, our</u> experiences
                                        A

    overseas <u>had made</u> us appreciate the <u>holiday's significance.</u> <u>No error.</u>
          B   **C**   **D**

18. Roger tried to ingratiate himself with the boss <u>by getting</u> to work <u>early and</u>
                 A   **B**

  volunteering for <u>overtime.</u> In addition to coming in half a day on Saturdays.
        C

  <u>No error.</u>
   D

19. Marc made a mess of the <u>trip.</u> He arrived at the airport late. He <u>didn't tip</u> the
          A   **B**

  baggage man (who promptly misdirected his bag), and he <u>loses</u> his wallet on the
                      C

  plane. <u>No error.</u>
    D

20. Four people saw the <u>accident, but</u> not one of them said <u>they</u> would be a witness for
         A   **B**

  <u>me in court.</u> <u>No error.</u>
   C   **D**

21. Andrea knew she had done <u>good</u> on the essay part of the <u>exam, but</u> she felt <u>bad</u>
            A   **B**   **C**

  about her performance on the objective questions. <u>No error.</u>
                 D

22. Social scientists <u>thinks</u> that <u>they have found</u> a direct correlation between television
        A   **B**

  watching and violent <u>behavior, not</u> only among children but also among adults.
          C

  <u>No error.</u>
   D

23. Everyone <u>who</u> goes to the <u>holiday parties</u> in our neighborhood <u>takes</u> a dish of food to
      A   **B**   **C**

  share. <u>No error.</u>
   D

24. The navy taught my dad how to be a plumber. <u>He's</u> not employed as a plumber
               A

  now, but he <u>does it</u> part-time to earn extra money. <u>No error.</u>
  <u>   </u> **C**   **D**
  B

25. It's not that Marcia <u>doesn't</u> understand the problem; she won't even accept <u>it's</u>
  <u> </u>   **B**   **C**
  A

  existence. <u>No error.</u>
     D

26. After <u>his</u> death, we discovered that my dad <u>had gave</u> over three thousand dollars a
         A   **B**

    <u>year to</u> his church. <u>No error.</u>
       C   **D**

27. The house next door sold for <u>$165,000 Martin</u> was <u>sure he</u> could get <u>more than</u> that
                                    A   **B**   **C**

    for his. <u>No error.</u>
           D

28. <u>The work of putting up</u> new gutters on old houses <u>require</u> several strong workers who
               A   **B**

    <u>are</u> not afraid of ladders. <u>No error.</u>
     C   **D**

29. Sandra Day <u>O'Connor,</u> the first woman appointed to the Supreme <u>Court was</u> chosen
               A   **B**

    by President Reagan in <u>1981.</u> Both Democrats and Republicans approved of the
                               C

    choice. <u>No error.</u>
           D

30. <u>Us</u> math students have to get <u>ourselves</u> organized if we hope to convince teachers to
   A   **B**

    change <u>their</u> requirements for this course. <u>No error.</u>
            C   **D**

31. As Toni <u>lay</u> down to take a nap, she <u>laid</u> her paycheck on the nightstand; it stayed
         A   **B**

    there for two days before she noticed it <u>lying</u> there. <u>No error.</u>
                                  C   **D**

32. The dentist <u>smiled when</u> he finished examining my teeth because he <u>knew, that</u> he
             A   **B**

    could retire for life once he <u>had taken care of</u> all my problems!
                           C

    <u>No error.</u>
       D

33. I would <u>like to</u> thank <u>whomever</u> is responsible for this lovely <u>luncheon</u> for our staff.
         A   **B**   **C**

    <u>No error.</u>
       D

34. Waiting for the children to fall asleep, we adults talked about the bedtime rituals we
    <u>A</u>   <u>B</u>
    had been <u>use</u> to in our own childhood. <u>No error.</u>
         <u>C</u>   <u>D</u>

35. Often a <u>child likes</u> to be read to because <u>they</u> get the <u>reader's</u> full attention.
         <u>A</u>   <u>B</u>   <u>C</u>
    <u>No error.</u>
       <u>D</u>

PART TWO

This part of the test has twenty-five sentences. Some of them are correct; others have errors in grammar or punctuation.

Each sentence has one underlined segment. Below the sentence are four ways of writing the underlined part. If the underlined segment is correct, choose A (No change). If the underlined segment needs to be corrected, choose the best way to write the underlined part and indicate the corresponding letter (B, C, or D) on your answer form.

EXAMPLE:

Picture books help a child develop recognition skills. By looking at the

picture, they learn how to connect what they see with what they read.

    A. No change.
    B. Picture books help children develop recognition skills. By looking at the picture, they learn
    C. Picture books help children develop recognition skills. By looking at the picture, he or she learns
    D. Picture books help a child develop recognition skills. By looking at the picture they learn

Answer: A   B   C   D
          ○   ●   ○   ○

---

36. Struggling, unpublished writers are sure that <u>publishers, who seek out and</u> <u>publish new authors,</u> are nonexistent.

    A. No change.
    B. publishers (who seek out and publish new authors)
    C. publishers — who seek out and publish new authors —
    D. publishers who seek out and publish new authors

37. By finishing the test items before time ran out, <u>a final recheck of his answers was</u> <u>possible for Gary.</u>

    A. No change.
    B. his answers could be given a final recheck by Gary.
    C. a final recheck could be given to his answers by Gary.
    D. Gary was able to give his answers a final recheck.

38. <u>A devoted father,</u> doing everything he could to make sure his children had all the things he had never had as a child.

    A. No change.
    B. A devoted father, because he was
    C. A devoted father, he was
    D. Being a devoted father,

39. The boys at St. Andrew's School had to wear suitcoats, starched shirts, and ties. <u>The girls uniforms</u> were much more comfortable.

    A. No change.
    B. The girl's uniforms
    C. The girl's uniform
    D. The girls' uniforms

40. In the baby pool the safety of the boys and girls <u>was</u> the responsibility of the parents, not the lifeguards.

    A. No change.
    B. were
    C. are
    D. have been

41. The Hudsons invited <u>my sister and me</u> to share a beach house on the Outer Banks in North Carolina.

    A. No change.
    B. my sister and I
    C. my sister and myself
    D. I and my sister

42. <u>Everyone who shops in this store reads</u> the magazines while they wait in the checkout line.

   A.   No change.
   B.   Everyone who shop in this store read
   C.   All customers who shop in this store read
   D.   Everybody who shops in this store reads

43. <u>Children whose last names begin with *A*, *B*, and *C*, teachers always choose them</u> to be first in line.

   A.   No change.
   B.   Always, children whose last names begin with *A*, *B*, and *C*, teachers choose them
   C.   Children whose last names begin with *A*, *B*, and *C*, always teachers choose them
   D.   Teachers always choose children whose last names begin with *A*, *B*, and *C*

44. Deirdre <u>only wanted her father to pay</u> her tuition, not all her college expenses.

   A.   No change.
   B.   wanted her father to pay only
   C.   wanted only her father to pay
   D.   wanted her father to only pay

45. There are four things I'd like to tell you about myself. I like <u>to cook, talk on the phone, working on computers, and going out on weekends.</u>

   A.   No change.
   B.   to cook, talking on the phone, working on computers, and going out on weekends.
   C.   cooking, talking on the phone, working on computers, and to go out on weekends.
   D.   to cook, talk on the phone, work on computers, and go out on weekends.

46. <u>Because the central air conditioner had broken the old fan and window units</u> were put into service.

   A.   No change.
   B.   Because the central air conditioner had broken the old fan, and window units
   C.   Because the central air conditioner had broken, the old fan and window units
   D.   Because the central air conditioner had broken the old fan and window units,

47. Passing the State Department's oral proficiency examination at level 2 is one thing, passing it at level 3 is something else altogether.

    A. No change.
    B. thing passing
    C. thing, however, passing
    D. thing; passing

48. My mom waited up for me and always asked whether I'd had a good time or not on my dates; she never stayed awake long enough to hear the answer.

    A. No change.
    B. dates, she
    C. dates; but she
    D. dates she

49. Angelissa was late because she failed to turn right at the traffic light her teacher had warned her about that intersection.

    A. No change.
    B. light; her
    C. light that her
    D. light, her

50. With her double major in physical education and nuclear medicine, Karima should be able to get a job either as a teacher or in a hospital setting.

    A. No change.
    B. she could work in a hospital setting.
    C. as a hospital worker.
    D. working in a hospital setting.

51. When the registrar looked at my eighteen-hour schedule, he asked me whether or not I also planned to work?

    A. No change.
    B. did I also plan to work.
    C. did I also plan to work?
    D. whether or not I also planned to work.

52. One way for parents to pass on their values to their children is to use opportunities that occur daily. Such as, chances to use the simple courtesies of "Please" and "Thank you."

    A. No change.
    B. daily; such as, chances
    C. daily. Such as: chances
    D. daily, such as chances

53. Although Sue Ann had grown up in a sheltered environment, but she quickly adapted to life in New York City.

    A. No change.
    B. environment, she
    C. environment; but she
    D. environment. But she

54. In each room of the restored palace were photographs of how the same room had looked after the damage done to the palace in World War II.

    A. No change.
    B. was
    C. is
    D. has been placed

55. Maurine advised her daughter to study tax law and accounting because certified public accountants are in great demand and are such a promising field.

    A. No change.
    B. able to command large salaries.
    C. such a lucrative position.
    D. a field just now opening up.

56. Nino cried when he saw the clown with the purple hair on stilts.

    A. No change.
    B. the purple-haired clown on stilts.
    C. the clown, who had purple hair on stilts.
    D. the clown walking on stilts with purple hair.

57. Major political problems may first show themselves in minor incidents. The Watergate episode, for instance, began with the discovery of a single piece of tape on the lock of a door. It led eventually to Richard Nixon's forced resignation as president of the United States.

    A. No change.
    B. episode for instance, began
    C. episode; for instance, began
    D. episode; for instance began

58. After Don and Sherry paid their household bills, and their next car payment, they had exactly twenty-two dollars left for food for two weeks.

    A. No change.
    B. bills; and their
    C. bills and, their
    D. bills and their

59. Alarmed by the possibility of surgery, every suggested exercise was practiced by the patient to postpone an operation.

    A.   No change.

    B.   postponing an operation required the patient to practice every suggested exercise.

    C.   an operation could be postponed by the patient by practicing every suggested exercise.

    D.   the patient practiced every suggested exercise to postpone an operation.

60. Before my English teacher would accept a paper, we had to prove that we had wrote an outline and at least two different drafts.

    A.   No change.

    B.   wrote

    C.   had written

    D.   have written

DIAGNOSTIC TEST
FORM B

This test of English skills has two parts. When you finish Part One, go directly to Part Two. You have forty-five minutes to respond to sixty items, so you should not spend too much time on any one item.

Each item has four possible answers. Choose the best answer and mark the appropriate space on your answer form, making sure to blacken the space thoroughly and to erase any stray pencil markings.

PART ONE

This part of the test has thirty-five sentences. Some of them are correct; others have errors in grammar or punctuation. No sentence has more than one error.

Each sentence has four underlined segments lettered A, B, C, and D. Read the sentence carefully. If there is a grammar or punctuation error in any of the underlined parts of the sentence, blacken the space that corresponds to the letter under the underlined segment. If there is no error, blacken the D space on your answer form.

EXAMPLE:

Salmon always return to <u>their</u> birthplace at egg-laying time. Strong currents
                          A

and high waterfalls in a <u>river does</u> not keep them from swimming upstream
                          B

<u>to lay</u> their eggs in that spot. <u>No error.</u>
  C   **D**

Answer: A   B   C   D

               ○   ●   ○   ○

---

1. When Harper decided to learn modern <u>jazz, not</u> the older <u>bluegrass, he</u> decided to
$\qquad$ **A** $\qquad\qquad$ **B**

go to New York <u>City not</u> Nashville. <u>No error.</u>
$\qquad$ **C** $\qquad\qquad$ **D**

2. After only <u>a week,</u> the new Parts Department clerk could check inventory
$\qquad$ **A**

<u>faster than</u> anyone <u>else. Because</u> she had memorized a hundred code numbers.
$\quad$ **B** $\qquad\qquad$ **C**

<u>No error.</u>
$\quad$ **D**

3. During his career, <u>which ended</u> two years ago, he <u>gave</u> more than five hundred
$\qquad\qquad$ **A** $\qquad\qquad\qquad$ **B**

performances. Now he <u>teaches</u> music. <u>No error.</u>
$\qquad\qquad$ **C** $\qquad$ **D**

4. Liz, like many people who <u>do</u> not own a car, <u>has</u> difficulty <u>carrying</u> her groceries back
$\qquad\qquad\qquad$ **A** $\qquad\qquad$ **B** $\qquad$ **C**

to her apartment. <u>No error.</u>
$\qquad\qquad$ **D**

5. We <u>are counting on</u> each team <u>that goes</u> to the tournament to do <u>their</u> best on the
$\qquad$ **A** $\qquad\qquad$ **B** $\qquad\qquad\qquad$ **C**

court. <u>No error.</u>
$\qquad$ **D**

6. <u>It's</u> no wonder that George and <u>him</u> failed physics; both devoted all their time to
$\;$ **A** $\qquad\qquad\qquad$ **B**

<u>sports, not schoolwork.</u> <u>No error.</u>
$\qquad$ **C** $\qquad$ **D**

7. <u>Alone,</u> Deeter thumbed through the newspaper while the TV blared <u>noisily</u> in the
$\;$ **A** $\qquad\qquad\qquad\qquad\qquad$ **B**

same room; when the phone rang, he reached for it <u>quick.</u> <u>No error.</u>
$\qquad\qquad\qquad\qquad\qquad$ **C** $\quad$ **D**

8. Whenever a dust storm <u>blew</u> in, people <u>drug</u> all their porch furniture inside and
$\qquad\qquad$ **A** $\qquad$ **B**

<u>drove</u> the horses and cows into the barn. <u>No error.</u>
$\;$ **C** $\qquad\qquad$ **D**

9. Many <u>Europeans think</u> that <u>American politicians</u> accomplish <u>hardly nothing</u> by their
$\qquad$ **A** $\qquad\qquad$ **B** $\qquad\qquad$ **C**

protracted congressional hearings. <u>No error.</u>
$\qquad\qquad$ **D**

10. Marian Anderson said that life had taught her to obey her own rules, to forget past
    $\overline{\text{A}}$ $\overline{\text{B}}$
    injustices, to sing her very best, and the importance of acting. No error.
                                  $\overline{\text{C}}$ $\overline{\text{D}}$

11. Five refugee families have arrived in our small town and their delight in our peaceful
                           $\overline{\text{A}}$ $\overline{\text{B}}$
    lives makes me happy that we decided to invite them. No error.
                       $\overline{\text{C}}$ $\overline{\text{D}}$

12. The senior finance officer in the firm was responsible for any decisions that dealt
        $\overline{\text{A}}$ $\overline{\text{B}}$
    with making donations to charities, moreover, that officer controlled political contri-
                              $\overline{\text{C}}$
    butions as well. No error.
                   $\overline{\text{D}}$

13. After age sixty, many Americans find they must adjust to: misplacing important
            $\overline{\text{A}}$ $\overline{\text{B}}$
    papers, forgetting people's names, gaining hard-to-lose pounds, and trying to con-
                                                        $\overline{\text{C}}$
    vince themselves that these problems are perfectly normal. No error.
                                                            $\overline{\text{D}}$

14. The little boy in Ezra Jack Keats book *Whistle for Willie,* who looks very much like the
                                $\overline{\text{A}}$
    sturdy, smiling child in *The Snowy Day,* also resembles Peter in *Peter's Chair.*
        $\overline{\text{B}}$ $\overline{\text{C}}$
    No error.
       $\overline{\text{D}}$

15. First, students should insert their disks. Next, they should turn on the computer.
                                $\overline{\text{A}}$ $\overline{\text{B}}$
    Then you wait for the screen to ask for the password. No error.
         $\overline{\text{C}}$ $\overline{\text{D}}$

16. Coach Blake, who ran for the first-aid kit, yelled at Mark to call 911 at
        $\overline{\text{A}}$ $\overline{\text{B}}$
    once. And told me to cover Kendall with my jacket. No error.
        $\overline{\text{C}}$ $\overline{\text{D}}$

17. Marianne watched the high school graduation ceremony with special interest this

    year, her return to school had made her understand the ritual's significance.
        $\overline{\text{A}}$ $\overline{\text{B}}$ $\overline{\text{C}}$
    No error.
       $\overline{\text{D}}$

18. Kelly attempted to get more <u>money for</u> the clerks by documenting their
A

<u>overtime and</u> comparing their jobs to other <u>jobs.</u> In addition to doing a time-and-
B   C

motion study on them. <u>No error.</u>
D

19. Joellyn activated the computer lab's terminals: First she turned on the main

<u>switch; then</u> she cleared all the screens. Finally, as she entered the code at the con-
A

trol terminal, she <u>couldn't suppress</u> a grin. Twenty-seven screens <u>flash</u> a four-color
B   C

"Welcome to the Lab" message. <u>No error.</u>
D

20. Three managers in our shop liked my proposal very <u>much, but</u> not one of them said
A

<u>they</u> would be a sponsor for <u>it at</u> the staff meeting. <u>No error.</u>
B   C   D

21. We felt <u>badly</u> about losing the <u>game, but</u> we all knew that we had played <u>well</u>.
A   B   C
<u>No error.</u>
D

22. After rearing several children, <u>parents realizes</u> that <u>they have learned</u> many
A   B

<u>lessons, not</u> only about the children but also about themselves. <u>No error.</u>
C   D

23. In our family, anyone <u>who</u> drives to the <u>ball games</u> at the park <u>offers</u> a ride to the
A   B   C

others. <u>No error.</u>
D

24. My sisters and I have always wanted to be opera singers. <u>We've</u> never become
A

stars, but we do <u>it</u> whenever we get together. <u>No error.</u>
B   C   D

25. <u>Isn't</u> it strange that a forbidden pleasure loses <u>its</u> allure when <u>its</u> no longer
A   B   C

forbidden? <u>No error.</u>
D

26. After his best friend's <u>wedding,</u> Eric discovered that he <u>had drank</u> far <u>too</u> many
                  A   **B**   **C**

    toasts. <u>No error.</u>
         D

27. The contestant in the first heat stayed underwater for only <u>sixty seconds I</u> was
                                                                    A

    <u>positive I</u> could last <u>longer</u> than that. <u>No error.</u>
      B   **C**   **D**

28. The <u>job of maneuvering</u> a tractor trailer through the mountains <u>demand</u> drivers who
                A   **B**

    have <u>strong nerves, quick reflexes, and good judgment.</u> <u>No error.</u>
       C   **D**

29. Mikhail <u>Gorbachev,</u> who took office in <u>1985 was</u> forced <u>to step down</u> after the failed
                 A   **B**   **C**

    coup attempt in 1991. <u>No error.</u>
                    D

30. <u>Us</u> faculty members have to agree among <u>ourselves</u> on how we want the deans to
     A   **B**

    change <u>their</u> timetable. <u>No error.</u>
           C   **D**

31. Two hours ago I put the quilt on the floor so that Chris could <u>lay</u> the baby on it
                                                   A

    and <u>lie</u> down himself; they have both been <u>lying</u> there ever since.
        B   **C**

    <u>No error.</u>
      D

32. The <u>blue jays</u> that like to eat bread off our <u>porch,</u> were chased <u>away by</u> our cat.
          A   **B**   **C**

    <u>No error.</u>
      D

33. The Rotarians <u>decided to honor</u> <u>whomever</u> had raised the most <u>money</u> for their eye
                    A   **B**   **C**

    care center. <u>No error.</u>
             D

34. When Lucille $\underline{\text{told}}$ the new $\underline{\text{man to}}$ unload the truck, the new man wanted to know
**A****B**

what he $\underline{\text{was suppose}}$ to do first. $\underline{\text{No error.}}$
**C**$$**D**

35. A book $\underline{\text{chosen}}$ by a child will keep $\underline{\text{their}}$ attention, so let a $\underline{\text{child choose}}$ the book to
**A**$$**B**$$**C**

be read aloud. $\underline{\text{No error.}}$
**D**

PART TWO

This part of the test has twenty-five sentences. Some of them are correct; others have errors in grammar or punctuation.

Each sentence has one underlined segment. Below the sentence are four ways of writing the underlined part. If the underlined segment is correct, choose A (No change). If the underlined segment needs to be corrected, choose the best way to write the underlined part and indicate the corresponding letter (B, C, or D) on your answer form.

EXAMPLE:

Picture books help a child develop recognition skills. By looking at the

picture, they learn how to connect what they see with what they read.

    A.   No change.
    B.   Picture books help children develop recognition skills. By looking at the picture, they learn
    C.   Picture books help children develop recognition skills. By looking at the picture, he or she learns
    D.   Picture books help a child develop recognition skills. By looking at the picture they learn

Answer: A   B   C   D
          ○   ●   ○   ○

---

36. Nonsmokers often assume that smokers, who want to quit, can do so fairly easily.

    A. No change.
    B. smokers (who want to quit)
    C. smokers — who want to quit —
    D. smokers who want to quit

37. After working feverishly to capture the prosecution's cross-examination, the new photographer's film was not accepted by the television station.

    A. No change.
    B. the television station would not accept the new photographer's film.
    C. the film of the new photographer was not accepted by the television station.
    D. the new photographer could not get the television station to accept her film.

38. An experienced player, putting all his expertise on the line to win this game.

    A. No change.
    B. An experienced player, because he was
    C. An experienced player, he was
    D. Being an experienced player,

39. The world's most productive industrial nations are known as the Group of Seven. These nations leaders meet each year.

    A. No change.
    B. The nation's leaders
    C. These nation's leader
    D. These nations' leaders

40. At Hillary's summer camp, the major activity for both the staff and the campers was backpacking in the mountains.

    A. No change.
    B. were
    C. are
    D. have been

41. The sergeant ordered my best buddy and me to stand guard duty on our night off.

    A. No change.
    B. my best buddy and I
    C. my best buddy and myself
    D. I and my best buddy

42. <u>Anyone who has Mr. Markham for senior English knows</u> on the first day that they will have a busy year ahead.

    A. No change.
    B. Anyone who have Mr. Markham for senior English know
    C. All students who have Mr. Markham for senior English know
    D. Everybody who has Mr. Markham for senior English knows

43. <u>Babies whose mothers breast-feed them, the mothers usually give them</u> immunity to some diseases.

    A. No change.
    B. Usually, babies whose mothers breast-feed them, the mothers give them
    C. Babies whose mothers breast-feed them, usually the mothers give them
    D. Mothers who breast-feed their babies usually give the babies

44. Steve's mother-in-law <u>only asked him to paint the porch windows,</u> not the whole porch.

    A. No change.
    B. asked him to paint only the porch windows
    C. asked only him to paint the porch windows
    D. asked him to only paint the porch windows

45. Picture books are important to a child in three ways: <u>to stimulate imagination, encouraging learning, and they are enjoyable.</u>

    A. No change.
    B. stimulating imagination, encouraging learning, and they are enjoyable.
    C. to stimulate imagination, to encourage learning, and they are enjoyable.
    D. They stimulate imagination, they encourage learning, and they are enjoy-able.

46. <u>After the workers had finished tearing off the old roof shingles and black paper scraps</u> were piled in the yard.

    A. No change.
    B. After the workers had finished tearing off the old roof shingles, and black paper scraps
    C. After the workers had finished tearing off the old roof, shingles and black paper scraps
    D. After the workers had finished tearing off the old roof shingles and black paper scraps,

47. The first three sections of the foreign service examination raised my hopes considerably, the last section dashed them completely.

    A. No change.
    B. considerably the
    C. considerably, however, the
    D. considerably; the

48. My sister's vacation routine never varied; she always basked in the sun for an hour before she helped set up camp.

    A. No change.
    B. varied, she
    C. varied; because she
    D. varied she

49. We lost the game because Nerida didn't pass to Carlyle when Carlyle was under the net the coach had told us to get the ball to Carlyle whenever he could score.

    A. No change.
    B. net; the coach
    C. net that the coach
    D. net, the coach

50. With his degree in engineering and his experience in the air force, David was sure he could get a job either as a pilot or in some kind of aviation engineering.

    A. No change.
    B. he could work in aviation engineering.
    C. as an aviation engineer.
    D. working as an aviation engineer.

51. Before Dad commented on my plan to get married after high school graduation, he asked me whether or not I planned to go to college and have a career?

    A. No change.
    B. did I plan to go to college and have a career.
    C. did I plan to go to college and have a career?
    D. whether or not I planned to go to college and have a career.

52. Most children have observed various forms of cheating that their families accept. Such as, the failure to report certain items on income tax forms.

    A. No change.
    B. accept; such as, the failure
    C. accept. Such as: failing
    D. accept, such as the failure

53. Since Sol delighted in physically difficult outdoor <u>activity, so, it</u> was logical for him to apply for the job of forest ranger.

    A. No change.
    B. activity, it
    C. activity; so it
    D. activity. So it

54. In the alley behind the burned houses <u>was</u> a small pile of furniture that the families had saved from the fire.

    A. No change.
    B. were
    C. are
    D. have been placed

55. I have gained hands-on experience that will help me <u>in my college courses and achieve my goals</u> in the business field.

    A. No change.
    B. do well in my college courses and achieve my goals
    C. in my college courses and in my goals
    D. in my college courses and to achieve my goals

56. <u>His name appeared on the list of men who were condemned to die on the governor's desk before 7:00 a.m.</u>

    A. No change.
    B. His name appeared on the list of men who were condemned to die; the list was on the governor's desk before 7:00 a.m.
    C. Before 7:00 a.m., his name appeared on the list of men who were condemned to die on the governor's desk.
    D. On the list of men who were condemned to die on the governor's desk before 7:00 a.m., his name appeared.

57. Important structural damage often appears first in small signs. A half-destroyed <u>joist, for example, may</u> reveal itself by a single carpenter ant.

    A. No change.
    B. joist for example, may
    C. joist; for example, may
    D. joist; for example may

58. Mom finished tearing out the overgrown ivy and bagging all the trash; then she discovered, that she had only twenty-two minutes to clean up and get dinner on the table.

    A. No change.
    B. discovered: that
    C. discovered; that
    D. discovered that

59. Convinced of his client's innocence, every possible tactic was used by the lawyer to delay the trial.

    A. No change.
    B. a delay of the trial was sought by every possible tactic by the lawyer.
    C. the trial was delayed by every possible tactic by the lawyer.
    D. the lawyer used every possible tactic to delay the trial.

60. Before the coach would accept our apologies, we had to convince him that we had ran five laps of the track.

    A. No change.
    B. ran
    C. had run
    D. have run

Part Four

DIAGNOSTIC TEST FORMS AA AND BB (WITH SOME ESL ITEMS)

FOR INSTRUCTORS: TOPICS TESTED
IN FORMS AA AND BB

A quarter of the questions test points of grammar and usage that are particularly troublesome to nonnative speakers of English; these questions are marked with an asterisk in the following list. All the other questions are the same as the corresponding items in forms A and B, respectively.

TEST ITEM	TOPIC TESTED	SECTION IN RULES FOR WRITERS	TEST ITEM	TOPIC TESTED	SECTION IN RULES FOR WRITERS
*1	Use of progressive	28	*33	Articles	29
2	Sentence fragment	19	34	-ed ending	27
3	Verb tense	27	35	Pronoun-antecedent agreement	22
4	Subject-verb agreement	21			
5	Pronoun-antecedent agreement	22	36	Comma (misuse of)	33
			37	Dangling modifier	12
6	Pronoun case	24	*38	Repeated subject	30
*7	Articles	29	39	Apostrophe	36
8	Verbs: irregular	27	40	Subject-verb agreement	21
9	Double negative	26	41	Pronoun case	24
10	Parallelism	9	42	Pronoun-antecedent agreement	22
11	Comma	32			
*12	Conditional sentence	28	43	Mixed construction	11
13	Colon (misuse of)	35	*44	Omitted expletive	30
14	Apostrophe	36	45	Parallelism	9
15	Shift	13	46	Comma	32
*16	Gerund/infinitive use	28	47	Run-on sentence	20
17	Run-on sentence	20	48	Semicolon	34
18	Sentence fragment	19	*49	Adjective and adverb placement	30
19	Shift	13			
20	Pronoun-antecedent agreement	22	*50	Articles	29
			51	Shift	13
21	Adjectives and adverbs	26	52	Sentence fragment	19
*22	Verb forms	28	53	Mixed construction	11
23	Subject-verb agreement	21	54	Subject-verb agreement	21
*24	Gerund/infinitive use	28	55	Mixed construction	11
25	Apostrophe	36	56	Misplaced modifier	12
*26	Articles	29	57	Comma	32
27	Run-on sentence	20	*58	Present and past participles	30
28	Subject-verb agreement	21			
*29	Repeated object	30	59	Dangling modifier	12
*30	Verb forms	28	60	Verbs: irregular	27
31	Verbs: *lie/lay*	27			
*32	Omitted verb	30			

Name _____ Section _____ Date _____

Instructor _____ Form _____

Instructions

1. Use only a No. 2 pencil.
2. Make a dark mark that completely fills the circle.
3. Erase cleanly.
4. Make no stray marks.

PART ONE   PART TWO

	A	B	C	D			A	B	C	D			A	B	C	D			A	B	C	D
1	○	○	○	○		19	○	○	○	○		36	○	○	○	○		49	○	○	○	○
2	○	○	○	○		20	○	○	○	○		37	○	○	○	○		50	○	○	○	○
3	○	○	○	○		21	○	○	○	○		38	○	○	○	○		51	○	○	○	○
4	○	○	○	○		22	○	○	○	○		39	○	○	○	○		52	○	○	○	○
5	○	○	○	○		23	○	○	○	○		40	○	○	○	○		53	○	○	○	○
6	○	○	○	○		24	○	○	○	○		41	○	○	○	○		54	○	○	○	○
7	○	○	○	○		25	○	○	○	○		42	○	○	○	○		55	○	○	○	○
8	○	○	○	○		26	○	○	○	○		43	○	○	○	○		56	○	○	○	○
9	○	○	○	○		27	○	○	○	○		44	○	○	○	○		57	○	○	○	○
10	○	○	○	○		28	○	○	○	○		45	○	○	○	○		58	○	○	○	○
11	○	○	○	○		29	○	○	○	○		46	○	○	○	○		59	○	○	○	○
12	○	○	○	○		30	○	○	○	○		47	○	○	○	○		60	○	○	○	○
13	○	○	○	○		31	○	○	○	○		48	○	○	○	○						
14	○	○	○	○		32	○	○	○	○												
15	○	○	○	○		33	○	○	○	○												
16	○	○	○	○		34	○	○	○	○												
17	○	○	○	○		35	○	○	○	○												
18	○	○	○	○																		

DIAGNOSTIC TEST
FORM AA

This test of English skills has two parts. When you finish Part One, go directly to Part Two. You have forty-five minutes to respond to sixty items, so you should not spend too much time on any one item.

Each item has four possible answers. Choose the best answer and mark the appropriate space on your answer form, making sure to blacken the space thoroughly and to erase any stray pencil markings.

PART ONE

This part of the test has thirty-five sentences. Some of them are correct; others have errors in grammar or punctuation. No sentence has more than one error.

Each sentence has four underlined segments lettered A, B, C, and D. Read the sentence carefully. If there is a grammar or punctuation error in any of the underlined parts of the sentence, blacken the space that corresponds to the letter under the underlined segment. If there is no error, blacken the D space on your answer form.

EXAMPLE:

Salmon always return to <u>their</u> birthplace at egg-laying time. Strong currents
                         A

and high waterfalls in a <u>river does</u> not keep them from swimming upstream
                          B

to <u>lay</u> their eggs in that spot. <u>No error.</u>
   C   **D**

Answer: A   B   C   D

            ○   ●   ○   ○

1. When the math teacher <u>asks for</u> volunteers, I <u>always raise</u> my hand; I <u>am knowing</u>
                       A   **B**   **C**

   how to solve almost any problem. <u>No error.</u>
                                D

2. The trainee for the <u>teller's position</u> was worried about his <u>speed and</u> unsure of his
                          A   **B**

   computer <u>skills. Until</u> he learned the new system. <u>No error.</u>
                   C   **D**

3. After Antigone <u>had buried</u> her brother, she <u>was brought</u> to the court and <u>questioned</u>
                         A   **B**   **C**

   by the king. <u>No error.</u>
                 D

4. Philip, unlike the thousands of students who <u>live</u> on campus, <u>has</u> to drive thirty
                                                 A   **B**

   miles each day <u>to reach</u> the university. <u>No error.</u>
                   C   **D**

5. The <u>modern American</u> family differs in <u>many significant</u> ways from <u>their</u> nineteenth-
                   A   **B**   **C**

   century counterpart. <u>No error.</u>
                        D

6. It's true that Sophie and <u>her</u> told Mark about the party, but <u>he</u> told the others.
   A   **B**   **C**

   <u>No error.</u>
    D

7. The flowers in our garden bloomed late this year because of the April snowstorm. It
    A   **B**

   has been <u>a</u> unusual spring. <u>No error.</u>
          C   **D**

8. Young Ben <u>swore</u> he would not cry as his father <u>drug</u> the nearly dead sheepdog
                A   **B**

   toward the barn; Ben <u>clung</u> to the dog's fur, trying to help. <u>No error.</u>
                     C   **D**

9. When the disc <u>jockey announced</u> the <u>winner's name</u>, Andrew <u>couldn't hardly</u> believe
                        A   **B**   **C**

   his ears. <u>No error.</u>
              D

10. Pablo <u>said that</u> sports <u>had taught him</u> to follow instructions, to prepare for games, to
         A   **B**

    adjust to new situations, <u>and the value of losing as well as winning.</u> <u>No error.</u>
                                 C   **D**

11. The seventeen-year locusts <u>have descended</u> on <u>our town and their</u> noise actually
                               A   **B**

    <u>drowns</u> out my daughter's music. <u>No error.</u>
      C   **D**

12. Whenever I <u>plan</u> to drive a long distance, <u>I check</u> my car's oil. If I didn't do this,
        A   **B**

    <u>I will</u> worry about ruining the engine. <u>No error.</u>
        C   **D**

13. Within the first thirty years of owning a <u>house, home owners</u> can count on having
                                                        A

    <u>to: replace</u> several major appliances, put on a new roof, contract for termite
        B

    <u>treatment, and</u> pay about a third of their income each year for the privilege of dealing
        C

    with all these problems. <u>No error.</u>
                                D

14. The <u>poets remark</u> about the longevity of <u>things of beauty did</u> not take into account
            A   **B**

    the <u>effects of</u> such phenomena as acid rain. <u>No error.</u>
            C   **D**

15. Drivers should first fasten <u>their</u> seat belts. Next <u>they should</u> put the key all the way
                                    A   **B**

    into the ignition. Then <u>you turn</u> the key to the right. <u>No error.</u>
                                C   **D**

16. When I <u>saw</u> Juan last night, I <u>asked</u> whether he had finished <u>to decorate</u> the house
            A   **B**   **C**

    for the party. <u>No error.</u>
                        D

17. We celebrated the Fourth of July with special fervor that <u>year, our</u> experiences over-
                                                                A

    seas <u>had made</u> us appreciate the <u>holiday's significance.</u> <u>No error.</u>
            B   **C**   **D**

18. Roger tried to ingratiate himself with the boss <u>by getting</u> to work <u>early and</u> volunteer-
                                                        A   **B**

    ing for <u>overtime. In</u> addition to coming in half a day on Saturdays. <u>No error.</u>
                C   **D**

19. Marc made a mess of the <u>trip:</u> He arrived at the airport late. He <u>didn't tip</u> the baggage
                                A   **B**

    man (who promptly misdirected his bag), and he <u>loses</u> his wallet on the plane.
                                                        C

    <u>No error.</u>
        D

20. Four people saw the <u>accident, but</u> not one of them said <u>they</u> would be a witness for
                            A   **B**

    <u>me in</u> court. <u>No error.</u>
        C   **D**

21. Andrea knew she had done <u>good</u> on the essay part of the <u>exam, but</u> she felt <u>bad</u>
                                  A   **B**   **C**

     about her performance on the objective questions. <u>No error.</u>
                                                   D

22. Getting more sleep <u>did not improving</u> her grades. She still <u>wasn't spending</u> enough
                                  A   **B**

     time <u>studying</u> for her exams. <u>No error.</u>
          C   **D**

23. Everyone <u>who</u> goes to the <u>holiday parties</u> in our neighborhood <u>takes</u> a dish of food to
               A   **B**   **C**

     share. <u>No error.</u>
            D

24. Each year many people decide <u>to quit</u> smoking. But how many people begin
                               A

     <u>smoking</u> during this same period? Researchers soon hope <u>answering</u> this question.
       B   **C**

     <u>No error.</u>
          D

25. <u>It's</u> not that Marcia <u>doesn't</u> understand the problem; she won't even accept <u>it's</u>
     A   **B**   **C**

     existence. <u>No error.</u>
                   D

26. My uncle Joe is <u>more like</u> a friend than a relative. He gives me <u>a good advice</u> when-
                  A   **B**

     ever I share <u>my problems</u> with him. <u>No error.</u>
                    C   **D**

27. The house next door sold for <u>$165,000 Martin</u> was <u>sure he</u> could get <u>more than</u> that
                                A   **B**   **C**

     for his. <u>No error.</u>
              D

28. <u>The work of putting up</u> new gutters on old houses <u>require</u> several strong workers who
                 A   **B**

     <u>are</u> not afraid of ladders. <u>No error.</u>
      C   **D**

29. The staff on a commercial airline needs <u>food that</u> is easy to <u>serve it</u>, so most of the
                                         A   **B**

     <u>meals come</u> in foil and plastic containers. <u>No error.</u>
         C   **D**

30. Jean likes to study languages. She <u>has been studied</u> French since high school. Next
                                          A

     semester she <u>will study</u> Spanish, and she <u>may study</u> German during the summer.
               B   **C**

     <u>No error.</u>
          D

31. As Toni lay down to take a nap, she laid her paycheck on the nightstand; it stayed
       A   B
    there for two days before she noticed it lying there. No error.
                                            C   D

32. When we went to the travel agency, we discovered that the airfare much too
                                          A   B
    expensive; therefore, we decided to go by train. No error.
         C   D

33. When I went to the visitors' bureau to ask for an information, I was told that none of
                    A   B
    the local hotels could provide us with a place to stay. No error.
                                          C   D

34. Waiting for the children to fall asleep, we adults talked about the bedtime rituals we
       A   B
    had been use to in our own childhood. No error.
           C   D

35. Often a child likes to be read to because they get the reader's full attention.
             A   B   C
    No error.
       D

PART TWO

This part of the test has twenty-five sentences. Some of them are correct; others have errors in grammar or punctuation.

Each sentence has one underlined segment. Below the sentence are four ways of writing the underlined part. If the underlined segment is correct, choose A (No change). If the underlined segment needs to be corrected, choose the best way to write the underlined part and indicate the corresponding letter (B, C, or D) on your answer form.

EXAMPLE:

Picture books help a child develop recognition skills. By looking at the

picture, they learn how to connect what they see with what they read.

    A.   No change.
    B.   Picture books help children develop recognition skills. By looking at the picture, they learn
    C.   Picture books help children develop recognition skills. By looking at the picture, he or she learns
    D.   Picture books help a child develop recognition skills. By looking at the picture they learn

Answer: A   B   C   D

                   ○   ●   ○   ○

---

36. Struggling, unpublished writers are sure that <u>publishers, who seek out and</u>

<u>publish new authors,</u> are nonexistent.

      A.   No change.
      B.   publishers (who seek out and publish new authors)
      C.   publishers — who seek out and publish new authors —
      D.   publishers who seek out and publish new authors

37. By finishing the test items before time ran out, <u>a final recheck of his answers was</u>

<u>possible for Gary.</u>

      A.   No change.
      B.   his answers could be given a final recheck by Gary.
      C.   a final recheck could be given to his answers by Gary.
      D.   Gary was able to give his answers a final recheck.

38. That attractive woman standing near the <u>fountain, she is</u> my French teacher.

      A.   No change.
      B.   fountain, is
      C.   fountain is
      D.   fountain she is

39. The boys at St. Andrew's School had to wear suitcoats, starched shirts, and ties.

<u>The girls uniforms</u> were much more comfortable.

      A.   No change.
      B.   The girl's uniforms
      C.   The girl's uniform
      D.   The girls' uniforms

40. In the baby pool, the safety of the boys and girls <u>was</u> the responsibility of the par-

ents, not the lifeguards.

      A.   No change.
      B.   were
      C.   are
      D.   have been

41. The Hudsons invited <u>my sister and me</u> to share a beach house on the Outer Banks

in North Carolina.

      A.   No change.
      B.   my sister and I
      C.   my sister and myself
      D.   I and my sister

42. <u>Everyone who shops in this store reads</u> the magazines while they wait in the checkout line.

    A.   No change.
    B.   Everyone who shop in this store read
    C.   All customers who shop in this store read
    D.   Everybody who shops in this store reads

43. <u>Children whose last names begin with *A*, *B*, and *C*, teachers always choose them</u> to be first in line.

    A.   No change.
    B.   Always, children whose last names begin with *A*, *B*, and *C*, teachers choose them
    C.   Children whose last names begin with *A*, *B*, and *C*, always teachers choose them
    D.   Teachers always choose children whose last names begin with *A*, *B*, and *C*

44. My father <u>always tells us is wrong</u> to lie, but he never reports all his income.

    A.   No change.
    B.   always tells us it is wrong
    C.   always tell us it is wrong
    D.   tells us always is wrong

45. There are four things I'd like to tell you about myself. I like <u>to cook, talk on the phone, working on computers, and going out on weekends.</u>

    A.   No change.
    B.   to cook, talking on the phone, working on computers, and going out on weekends.
    C.   cooking, talking on the phone, working on computers, and to go out on weekends.
    D.   to cook, talk on the phone, work on computers, and go out on weekends.

46. <u>Because the central air conditioner had broken the old fan and window units</u> were put into service.

    A.   No change.
    B.   Because the central air conditioner had broken the old fan, and window units
    C.   Because the central air conditioner had broken, the old fan and window units
    D.   Because the central air conditioner had broken the old fan and window units,

47. Passing the State Department's oral proficiency examination at level 2 is one thing, passing it at level 3 is something else altogether.

    A. No change.
    B. thing passing
    C. thing, however, passing
    D. thing; passing

48. My mom waited up for me and always asked whether I'd had a good time or not on my dates; she never stayed awake long enough to hear the answer.

    A. No change.
    B. dates, she
    C. dates; but she
    D. dates she

49. Beyond the village was an old large bridge that crossed a little ugly creek.

    A. No change.
    B. a large old bridge that crossed an ugly little creek.
    C. an old large bridge that crossed an ugly little creek.
    D. a large old bridge that crossed a little ugly creek.

50. At the zoo, we saw only one man watching the monkeys; he was making funny faces at them. A man laughed when one of the monkeys made a face back at him.

    A. No change.
    B. Man laughed
    C. The man laughed
    D. Any man laughed

51. When the registrar looked at my eighteen-hour schedule, he asked me whether or not I also planned to work?

    A. No change.
    B. did I also plan to work.
    C. did I also plan to work?
    D. whether or not I also planned to work.

52. One way for parents to pass on their values to their children is to use opportunities that occur daily. Such as, chances to use the simple courtesies of "Please" and "Thank you."

    A. No change.
    B. daily; such as, chances
    C. daily. Such as: chances
    D. daily, such as chances

53. Although Sue Ann had grown up in a sheltered <u>environment, but she</u> quickly adapted to life in New York City.

    A. No change.
    B. environment, she
    C. environment; but she
    D. environment. But she

54. In each room of the restored palace <u>were</u> photographs of how the same room had looked after the damage done to the palace in World War II.

    A. No change.
    B. was
    C. is
    D. has been placed

55. Maurine advised her daughter to study tax law and accounting because certified public accountants are in great demand and are <u>such a promising field.</u>

    A. No change.
    B. able to command large salaries.
    C. such a lucrative position.
    D. a field just now opening up.

56. Nino cried when he saw <u>the clown with the purple hair on stilts.</u>

    A. No change.
    B. the purple-haired clown on stilts.
    C. the clown, who had purple hair on stilts.
    D. the clown walking on stilts with purple hair.

57. Major political problems may first show themselves in minor incidents. The Watergate <u>episode, for instance, began</u> with the discovery of a piece of tape on the lock of a door. It led eventually to Richard Nixon's forced resignation as president of the United States.

    A. No change.
    B. episode for instance, began
    C. episode; for instance, began
    D. episode; for instance began

58. The presidency of John F. Kennedy <u>was both an excited and frightening period</u> in American history.

    A. No change.
    B. was both an excited and frightened period
    C. was both an exciting and frightened period
    D. was both an exciting and frightening period

59. Alarmed by the possibility of surgery, <u>every suggested exercise was practiced by the patient to postpone an operation.</u>

    A. No change.
    B. postponing an operation required the patient to practice every suggested exercise.
    C. an operation could be postponed by the patient by practicing every suggested exercise.
    D. the patient practiced every suggested exercise to postpone an operation.

60. Before my English teacher would accept a paper, we had to prove that we <u>had wrote</u> an outline and at least two different drafts.

    A. No change.
    B. wrote
    C. had written
    D. have written

DIAGNOSTIC TEST
FORM BB

This test of English skills has two parts. When you finish Part One, go directly to Part Two. You have forty-five minutes to respond to sixty items, so you should not spend too much time on any one item.

Each item has four possible answers. Choose the best answer and mark the appropriate space on your answer form, making sure to blacken the space thoroughly and to erase any stray pencil markings.

PART ONE

This part of the test has thirty-five sentences. Some of them are correct; others have errors in grammar or punctuation. No sentence has more than one error.

Each sentence has four underlined segments lettered A, B, C, and D. Read the sentence carefully. If there is a grammar or punctuation error in any of the underlined parts of the sentence, blacken the space that corresponds to the letter under the underlined segment. If there is no error, blacken the D space on your answer form.

EXAMPLE:

> Salmon always return to their birthplace at egg-laying time. Strong cur-
>   **A**
>
> rents and high waterfalls in a river does not keep them from swimming
>   **B**
>
> upstream to lay their eggs in that spot. No error.
>   **C**   **D**

Answer: A   B   C   D
                ○   ●   ○   ○

1. When the policeman <u>asks for</u> my car registration, I <u>always have</u> it handy; I

                A   **B**

   <u>am believing</u> in being prepared. <u>No error.</u>

       C   **D**

2. After only a <u>week,</u> the new Parts Department clerk could check inventory

              A

   <u>faster than</u> anyone <u>else. Because</u> she had memorized a hundred code numbers.

        B   **C**

   <u>No error.</u>

     D

3. During his career, <u>which ended</u> two years ago, he <u>gave</u> more than five hundred

                  A   **B**

   performances. Now <u>he teaches</u> music. <u>No error.</u>

              C   **D**

4. Liz, like many people who <u>do</u> not own a car, <u>has</u> difficulty <u>carrying</u> her groceries

                           A   **B**   **C**

   back to her apartment. <u>No error.</u>

                  D

5. <u>We are counting on</u> each team <u>that goes</u> to the tournament to do <u>their</u> best on the

            A   **B**   **C**

   court. <u>No error.</u>

       D

6. <u>It's</u> no wonder that George and <u>him</u> failed physics; both devoted all their time to

   A   **B**

   sports, <u>not schoolwork.</u> <u>No error.</u>

            C   **D**

7. As <u>a</u> boy, he learned from his father how to chop wood with <u>an</u> ax. Later, this proved

      A   **B**

   to be <u>an</u> useful skill. <u>No error.</u>

        C   **D**

8. Whenever a dust storm <u>blew</u> in, people <u>drug</u> all their porch furniture inside and

                     A   **B**

   <u>drove</u> the horses and cows into the barn. <u>No error.</u>

    C   **D**

9. Many Europeans think that American politicians don't accomplish hardly nothing
   _____   _____   _____
          A   B   C
   by their protracted congressional hearings. No error.
                                              _____
                                                 D

10. Marian Anderson said that life had taught her to obey her own rules, to forget past
    _____ _____   _____
                       A   B
    injustices, to sing her very best, and the importance of acting. No error.
                                          _____   _____
                                                   C   D

11. Five refugee families have arrived in our small town and their delight in our peaceful
                        _____   _____
                              A   B
    lives makes me happy that we decided to invite them. No error.
                    _____   _____
                          C   D

12. Someday I'd like to establish my own business. If I had the capital, I will do it now.
            ___   _____   _____
             A   B   C
    No error.
    _____
       D

13. After age sixty, many Americans find they must adjust to: misplacing important
              _____   _____
                   A   B
    papers, forgetting people's names, gaining hard-to-lose pounds, and trying to con-
                                                           _____
                                                              C
    vince themselves that these problems are perfectly normal. No error.
                                                              _____
                                                                 D

14. The little boy in Ezra Jack Keats book *Whistle for Willie*, who looks very much like the
                               _____
                                     A
    sturdy, smiling child in *The Snowy Day,* also resembles Peter in *Peter's Chair.*
    _____   _____
           B   C
    No error.
    _____
       D

15. First, students should insert their disks. Next, they should turn on the computer.
                                _____   _____
                                  A   B
    Then you wait for the screen to ask for the password. No error.
        _____   _____
           C   D

16. I expect to take my exam in October. Originally I had planned to take the exam in
    _____   _____
           A   B
    August, but I decided postponing it when I realized I would need more time to
                 _____
                        C
    prepare. No error.
            _____
               D

17. Marianne watched the high school graduation ceremony with special interest this

    year, her return to school <u>had made</u> her understand <u>the ritual's</u> significance.
    <u>   </u>   **B**   **C**

      A

    <u>No error.</u>
      D

18. Kelly attempted to get more <u>money for</u> the clerks by documenting their <u>overtime and</u>
                                A   **B**

    comparing their jobs to other <u>jobs.</u> In addition to doing a time-and-motion study on
                                        C

    them. <u>No error.</u>
         D

19. Joellyn activated the computer lab's terminals: First she turned on the main

    <u>switch; then</u> she cleared all the screens. Finally, as she entered the code at the con-
      A

    trol terminal, she <u>couldn't suppress</u> a grin. Twenty-seven screens <u>flash</u> a four-color
                      B   **C**

    "Welcome to the Lab" message. <u>No error.</u>
                          D

20. Three managers in our shop liked my proposal very <u>much, but</u> not one of them said
                                                  A

    <u>they</u> would be a sponsor for <u>it at</u> the staff meeting. <u>No error.</u>
      B   **C**   **D**

21. We felt <u>badly</u> about losing the <u>game, but</u> we all knew that we had played <u>well.</u>
            A   **B**   **C**

    <u>No error.</u>
      D

22. Even though she <u>was take</u> the medicine, her fever <u>rose</u> throughout the afternoon and
                      A   **B**

    <u>reached</u> 103 degrees by evening. <u>No error.</u>
      C   **D**

23. In our family, anyone <u>who</u> drives to the <u>ball games</u> at the park <u>offers</u> a ride to the
                          A   **B**   **C**

    others. <u>No error.</u>
          D

24. He planned <u>to retire</u> at age sixty-two, but his boss asked him <u>to work</u> two more years.
           A   **B**

    When he refused, his boss offered <u>increasing</u> his salary. <u>No error.</u>
                                  C   **D**

25. Isn't it strange that a forbidden pleasure loses <u>its</u> allure when <u>its</u> no longer

A   B   C

    forbidden? <u>No error.</u>

           D

26. Louisiana is <u>more like</u> the tropics than many people realize. Though the state occa-

            A

    sionally has <u>a nice, dry weather,</u> <u>its rainy season</u> lasts all year. <u>No error.</u>

        B   C   D

27. The contestant in the first heat stayed underwater for only <u>sixty seconds</u> I was

                                          A

    <u>positive</u> I could last <u>longer than</u> that. <u>No error.</u>

 B   C   D

28. <u>The job of maneuvering</u> a tractor trailer through the mountains <u>demand</u> drivers who

        A   B

    <u>have</u> strong nerves, quick reflexes, and good judgment. <u>No error.</u>

 C   D

29. She became ill because she drank <u>water that</u> she hadn't <u>boiled it.</u> When she got back

                              A   B

    home, <u>she had</u> to see a doctor. <u>No error.</u>

     C   D

30. We <u>should to eat less</u> fast food. Tonight we <u>will eat</u> some fish and fresh vegetables,

          A   B

    and we <u>may eat</u> the same thing tomorrow. <u>No error.</u>

      C   D

31. Two hours ago I put the quilt on the floor so that Chris could <u>lay</u> the baby on it and

                                               A

    <u>lie</u> down himself; they have both been <u>lying</u> there ever since. <u>No error.</u>

 B   C   D

32. When we returned from our vacation, <u>we realized</u> that the <u>door wide open.</u>

                                  A   B

    Fortunately, <u>nothing had been</u> stolen. <u>No error.</u>

           C   D

33. Because of <u>the</u> recession, he had a hard time finding <u>an</u> employment. Finally he got a

          A   B

    job with <u>the</u> government. <u>No error.</u>

        C   D

34. When Lucille <u>told</u> the new <u>man to</u> unload the truck, the new man wanted to know

               A   **B**

    what he <u>was suppose</u> to do first. <u>No error.</u>

             C   **D**

35. A book <u>chosen</u> by a child will keep <u>their</u> attention, so let a <u>child choose</u> the book to

          A   **B**   **C**

    be read aloud. <u>No error.</u>

             D

PART TWO

This part of the test has twenty-five sentences. Some of them are correct; others have errors in grammar or punctuation.

Each sentence has one underlined segment. Below the sentence are four ways of writing the underlined part. If the underlined segment is correct, choose A (No change). If the underlined segment needs to be corrected, choose the best way to write the underlined part and indicate the corresponding letter (B, C, or D) on your answer form.

EXAMPLE:

Picture books help a child develop recognition skills. By looking at the

picture, they learn how to connect what they see with what they read.

- A. No change.
- B. Picture books help children develop recognition skills. By looking at the picture, they learn
- C. Picture books help children develop recognition skills. By looking at the picture, he or she learns
- D. Picture books help a child develop recognition skills. By looking at the picture they learn

Answer: A   B   C   D
           ○   ●   ○   ○

Form BB   87

36. Nonsmokers often assume that smokers, who want to quit, can do so fairly easily.

    A. No change.
    B. smokers (who want to quit)
    C. smokers — who want to quit —
    D. smokers who want to quit

37. After working feverishly to capture the prosecution's cross-examination, the new photographer's film was not accepted by the television station.

    A. No change.
    B. the television station would not accept the new photographer's film.
    C. the film of the new photographer was not accepted by the television station.
    D. the new photographer could not get the television station to accept her film.

38. The Mississippi River system it is the third largest in the world.

    A. No change.
    B. system, is
    C. system is
    D. system, it is

39. The world's most productive industrial nations are known as the Group of Seven. These nations leaders meet each year.

    A. No change.
    B. These nation's leaders
    C. These nation's leader
    D. These nations' leaders

40. At Hillary's summer camp, the major activity for both the staff and the campers was backpacking in the mountains.

    A. No change.
    B. were
    C. are
    D. have been

41. The sergeant ordered my best buddy and me to stand guard duty on our night off.

    A. No change.
    B. my best buddy and I
    C. my best buddy and myself
    D. I and my best buddy

42. Anyone who has Mr. Markham for senior English knows on the first day that they will have a busy year ahead.

    A. No change.
    B. Anyone who have Mr. Markham for senior English know
    C. All students who have Mr. Markham for senior English know
    D. Everybody who has Mr. Markham for senior English knows

43. Babies whose mothers breast-feed them, the mothers usually give them immunity to some diseases.

    A. No change.
    B. Usually, babies whose mothers breast-feed them, the mothers give them
    C. Babies whose mothers breast-feed them, usually, the mothers give them
    D. Mothers who breast-feed their babies usually give the babies

44. My brother always says is easy to find a date, but he's never been a girl.

    A. No change.
    B. always says it is easy
    C. always say it is easy
    D. says always is easy

45. Picture books are important to a child in three ways: to stimulate imagination, encouraging learning, and they are enjoyable.

    A. No change.
    B. stimulating imagination, encouraging learning, and they are enjoyable.
    C. to stimulate imagination, to encourage learning, and they are enjoyable.
    D. They stimulate imagination, they encourage learning, and they are enjoyable.

46. After the workers had finished tearing off the old roof shingles and black paper scraps were piled in the yard.

    A. No change.
    B. After the workers had finished tearing off the old roof shingles, and black paper scraps
    C. After the workers had finished tearing off the old roof, shingles and black paper scraps
    D. After the workers had finished tearing off the old roof shingles and black paper scraps,

47. The first three sections of the foreign service examination raised my hopes considerably, the last section dashed them completely.

    A. No change.
    B. considerably the
    C. considerably, however, the
    D. considerably; the

48. My sister's vacation routine never varied; she always basked in the sun for an hour before she helped set up camp.

    A. No change.
    B. varied, she
    C. varied; because she
    D. varied she

49. An enormous old oak tree with green large leaves stood outside her house.

    A. No change.
    B. An enormous old oak tree with large green leaves
    C. An old enormous oak tree with green large leaves
    D. An old enormous oak tree with large green leaves

50. After the movie, we went to a restaurant on Bright Street. A restaurant was called Charlie's.

    A. No change.
    B. Restaurant
    C. The restaurant
    D. Some restaurant

51. Before Dad commented on my plan to get married after high school graduation, he asked me whether or not I planned to go to college and have a career?

    A. No change.
    B. did I plan to go to college and have a career.
    C. did I plan to go to college and have a career?
    D. whether or not I planned to go to college and have a career.

52. Most children have observed various forms of cheating that their families accept. Such as, the failure to report certain items on income tax forms.

    A. No change.
    B. accept; such as, the failure
    C. accept. Such as: failing
    D. accept, such as the failure

53. Since Sol delighted in physically difficult outdoor <u>activity, so, it</u> was logical for him to apply for the job of forest ranger.

    A. No change.
    B. activity, it
    C. activity; so it
    D. activity. So it

54. In the alley behind the burned houses <u>was</u> a small pile of furniture that the families had saved from the fire.

    A. No change.
    B. were
    C. are
    D. have been placed

55. I have gained hands-on experience that will help me <u>in my college courses and achieve my goals</u> in the business field.

    A. No change.
    B. do well in my college courses and achieve my goals
    C. in my college courses and in my goals
    D. in my college courses and to achieve my goals

56. <u>His name appeared on the list of men who were condemned to die on the governor's desk before 7:00 a.m.</u>

    A. No change.
    B. His name appeared on the list of men who were condemned to die; the list was on the governor's desk before 7:00 a.m.
    C. Before 7:00 a.m., his name appeared on the list of men who were condemned to die on the governor's desk.
    D. On the list of men who were condemned to die on the governor's desk before 7:00 a.m., his name appeared.

57. Important structural damages often appear first in small signs. A half-destroyed <u>joist, for example, may</u> reveal itself by a single carpenter ant.

    A. No change.
    B. joist for example, may
    C. joist; for example, may
    D. joist; for example may

58.   The work was <u>exciting, but she was exhausting</u> by the end of the day.

   A.   No change.
   B.   excited, but she was exhausted
   C.   exciting, and she was exhausting
   D.   exciting, but she was exhausted

59.   Convinced of his client's innocence, <u>every possible tactic was used by the lawyer to delay the trial.</u>

   A.   No change.
   B.   a delay of the trial was sought by every possible tactic by the lawyer.
   C.   the trial was delayed by every possible tactic by the lawyer.
   D.   the lawyer used every possible tactic to delay the trial.

60.   Before the coach would accept our apologies, we had to convince him that we <u>had ran</u> five laps of the track.

   A.   No change.
   B.   ran
   C.   had run
   D.   have run

Answers to Quizzes

Quiz 8-1: Active verbs

Possible revisions:

1. The coach asked two players to visit local schools.
2. We learned from the survey that our staff wanted more training.
3. The label warns patients taking this medication not to drink alcohol.
4. CareAmerica will give more than one million dollars to disaster survivors.
5. For as long as I can remember, we have said grace before every meal at our house.
6. The local police showed no courtesy at all to the peaceful protesters.
7. We can conclude that a college education provides a significant economic advantage.
8. Landlords who want to avoid making repairs often deny housing to families with children.
9. The commission is investigating six complaints against the retail chain.
10. The principal punished the students before giving them a chance to explain.

Quiz 9-1: Parallelism

Possible revisions:

1. Ari helped by painting the fence, trimming shrubs, mulching flowerbeds, and raking leaves.
2. Sebastian liked playing video games more than watching television.
3. The computer salesperson promised that I would receive not only a rebate but also a free iPod.
4. Rina was hired to stock merchandise, write orders for delivery, and sell computers.
5. Michiko told the judge that she had been pulled out of a line of fast-moving traffic and that she had a perfect driving record.
6. To administer the poison, the tribe's sorcerers put it in their victims' food, throw it into their huts, or drop it into their mouths or nostrils while they sleep.
7. Sylvia loved swimming, canoeing, and hiking.
8. Julius realized that he was a talented violinist but that proper training and discipline would be the best foundation for a career as a musician.
9. Bill found that it was harder to be fair to himself than to be fair to others.
10. At the arts-and-crafts table, the children make potholders and key rings, weave baskets, paint pictures, and assemble model cars.

Quiz 10-1: Needed words

Possible revisions:

1. As Luis began cooking, he noticed that his friend's vintage 1950s oven wasn't working properly.
2. For many years Americans had trust in and affection for Walter Cronkite.
3. Years of skateboarding made Jason's reflexes much sharper than his brother's.
4. The study showed that tenth graders are more polite to strangers than ninth graders are. *Or* The study showed that tenth graders are more polite to strangers than they are to ninth graders.
5. My adviser was someone whom I saw frequently on campus but who never seemed to be in his office.
6. The cougar's eyeball, pupil, and lens are proportionately larger than those of other carnivores.
7. When the fishing trip was canceled, my dad was as disappointed as, if not more disappointed than, his granddaughter.
8. Phyllis says that she never has registered to vote in the primaries and never will register.
9. To patch a deep hole, work the first coat of patching into place with a putty knife, pressing in the plaster.
10. Uncle Cecil's pies won far more prizes than Aunt Margaret's.

Quiz 11-1: Mixed constructions

Possible revisions:

1. Astronomy, an ancient science, was especially important to agricultural societies.
2. Pushing the button for the insert mode opens the computer's CD-ROM drive.
3. Being exposed to summer sun without protection can be dangerous.
4. The reason Frank burned the bread is that he was talking on the telephone.
5. Thailand has one of the fastest growing stock exchanges in the world.

6. Floyd Fay failed a polygraph test and demanded a second one, which he also failed.
7. Who would have thought that working as a department store salesperson could be a life-threatening job?
8. In Seoul, Korea, you can get exceptional bargains — if you are prepared to negotiate.
9. The number of applications is increasing rapidly.
10. The area near the victim's garage provided the investigators with several important clues.

Quiz 12-1: Misplaced and dangling modifiers

Possible revisions:

1. At her deathbed, he promised never to remarry.
2. In late 1973, the major oil producers shocked the nation by putting an embargo on crude oil sent to the United States.
3. Although the rescued infant was wearing only a diaper, the EMT reported that the infant had no signs of hypothermia.
4. At the next train stop, not all doors will open. [*Some doors will open.*]
5. Señor Tejada is prepared to fly to Belize as soon as possible.
6. As the train reached the border, all passengers were asked to have their passports ready.
7. After Jason had lived more than ten years on the streets, social workers persuaded him to take one of the new medications for schizophrenia.
8. This form is required only when the traveler is receiving an advance.
9. The fund is designed for those who want to gain above-average returns quickly.
10. Thinking that justice had finally prevailed, Lydia realized that her troubles were just beginning.

Quiz 13-1: Shifts

Possible revisions:

1. Pilots flying in bad weather rely on their instruments for safe navigation.
2. On Saturday we cleaned the attic and discovered a bundle of love letters we knew would embarrass our parents.
3. Ming-Na told me she could convert my CDs to MP3 format and asked when she could come over to get started.
4. Our class visited a museum of living history, where we saw how people had lived in a nineteenth-century village. We participated in several activities. For example, we were shown how to spin and weave.
5. We always follow the same routine at the campground. First, we erect the tent, roll out the sleeping bags, and set up the kitchen; then we all head for the swimming pool.
6. Police officers follow strict codes of safety. For example, they always point the barrel of the gun upward when the gun is not in use.
7. You should get to the stadium early unless you want to stand in line with mobs of people waiting for tickets.
8. We wondered whether the water was clean enough to drink and whether we could swim in it.
9. With a little self-discipline and a desire to improve yourself, you too can enjoy the benefits of running.
10. One tour guide collects the tickets and another gives out the maps.

Quiz 14-1: Choppy sentences

Possible revisions:

1. My grandmother left the house before I got home every Tuesday because she sang in the local jazz club.
2. Although his famous kite experiment was extremely dangerous, it gave Franklin important insights into the nature of electricity.
3. Anesh told her boss she would manage the project even though it was behind schedule and understaffed.
4. Although the Web site looked professional and was sponsored by an organization that sounded reputable, we soon realized that it was full of misinformation.
5. Well-protected, the human heart lies behind the breastbone, between the lungs, and above the diaphragm, a tough layer of muscle.
6. My mother is trying to cut down on the fat in her diet, so she uses yogurt instead of oil.
7. Every day Sisyphus helplessly repeated the same meaningless task, pushing a heavy stone up a steep mountain. He then stepped aside and watched as it rolled back down again.
8. Although their workhorse was used primarily for pulling the plow, their daughter sometimes rode it through the woods to visit the neighbors.

Answers to Quizzes   93

9. The Web site offers summaries of articles that have appeared in the past three issues, but the site charges for access to the full text of the articles.
10. When table tennis, also known as Ping-Pong, became an Olympic sport in 1988, my brother was inspired to begin practicing.

Quiz 19-1:   Sentence fragments

Possible revisions:

1. English has borrowed many words from Spanish, such as *adobe*, *bravado*, and *mosquito*.
2. After my test drive, I came to a conclusion — that purchasing a hybrid vehicle was a smart move.
3. As we walked up the path, we came upon the gun barrels, large gray concrete structures covered with ivy and weeds.
4. Standardized testing has produced a great deal of apprehension among elementary school teachers. Many teachers, in fact, have considered petitioning the education department.
5. Correct
6. I felt caught between two worlds, the world of my urban neighborhood and the world of my suburban college campus.
7. Keiko arrived in the village of Futagami, where she was to spend the summer with her grandparents.
8. I had pushed these fears into one of those quiet places in my mind, hoping they would stay there asleep.
9. Aspiring bodybuilders must first determine their strengths and weaknesses and then decide what they want to achieve.
10. The side effects of lithium are many: nausea, stomach cramps, thirst, muscle weakness, vomiting, diarrhea, confusion, and tremors.

Quiz 20-1:   Run-on sentences

Possible revisions:

1. Shoshana renewed her driver's license, and a day later she lost it.
2. The world of digital music is incredibly flexible; people can even download songs to a cell phone.
3. Correct
4. The suburbs seemed cold; they lacked the warmth and excitement of our Italian neighborhood.
5. Monument Beach was closed for the day, so we decided to see a movie.
6. Why should we pay taxes to support public transportation? We prefer to save energy by carpooling.
7. After days of struggling with her dilemma, Rosa came to a decision: She would sacrifice herself for her people and her cause.
8. While we were walking down Grover Avenue, Gary told us about his Aunt Elsinia, who was an extraordinary woman.
9. After the rain had stopped, we staked the outline of the path and broke the ground by late morning. Then we tamped down the earth, laid the gravel, and set the bricks in place.
10. Paloma is an experienced guide who will answer any questions you might have about the history and geography of the region.

Quiz 21-1:   Subject-verb agreement

Possible revisions:

1. The peeling paint and the broken railing make our home appear older than its twenty years.
2. Correct
3. The most significant lifesaving device in automobiles is air bags.
4. There are several cups of tea on the table.
5. Correct
6. Only one of the many architectural treatises written in antiquity survives.
7. Every year a number of kokanee salmon, not native to the region, are introduced into Flathead Lake.
8. Correct
9. Correct
10. At MGM Studios at Disney World, the wonders of moviemaking come alive.

Quiz 22-1:   Pronoun-antecedent agreement

Possible revisions:

1. The group was expected to travel as a unit and make its plans by consensus.
2. When clients come to the writing center, they should feel comfortable enough to seek advice.
3. The National Organization for Women was founded in 1966. That same year, the organization fought sex discrimination in the airline industry.
4. Irina gave the book to someone who lent it to a relative.
5. Anybody who wishes to pay by check should see the manager for approval.

6. No one should be forced to sacrifice his or her prized possession — life — for someone else.
7. The board of directors was unanimous in its decision to offer health benefits to part-time workers.
8. Good teachers are patient with their students, and they maintain an even temper.
9. Correct
10. On the first day of class, Mr. Bhatti asked the students why they wanted to stop smoking.

Quiz 23-1:   Pronoun reference

Possible revisions:

1. In *My Sister's Keeper*, Jodi Picoult explores medical ethics.
2. If you have a sweet tooth, visit the confectioner's shop, where candy is still made as it was a hundred years ago.
3. The Registry of Motor Vehicles is more user-friendly now. It even allows individuals to renew licenses online.
4. After working in the apple orchard all morning, we took a bushel of apples home to eat.
5. He recognized her as the woman who had won an Olympic gold medal for swimming.
6. Juan told Jeremy, "I have been promoted."
7. In his poetry, John Donne often juxtaposes the sacred with the profane.
8. In Saudi Arabia it is considered ill mannered for a person to reject a gift.
9. When Tia Elena put the cake on the table, the cake collapsed. *Or* When Tia Elena put the cake on the table, the table collapsed.
10. Be sure to visit Istanbul's bazaar, where vendors sell everything from Persian rugs to electronic calculators.

Quiz 24-1:   Pronoun case (such as *I* versus *me*)

Possible revisions:

1. Professor Gerroir gave Marlo and me the opportunity to conduct field research.
2. Correct
3. Jasmine can't come to the party because she and her brother will be out of town that day.
4. I am jealous that our dog likes my neighbor more than me.
5. Doctors should take more seriously what we patients say about our treatment.
6. Randy came with my grandfather and me to the baseball game.
7. Correct
8. It is strange how people in other countries often seem much happier than we. *Or* It is strange how people in other countries often seem much happier than we are.
9. I am sure that we will all be scolded for John's laughing during the most solemn moment of the ceremony.
10. My older sister promised to leave her old laptop behind for Paulette and me.

Quiz 25-1:   *Who* versus *whom*

Possible revisions:

1. I hope you like Kendra, who is also coming to lunch.
2. Correct
3. They will become business partners with whoever is willing to contribute to the company's coffers.
4. Correct
5. The elderly woman whom I was asked to take care of was a clever, delightful companion.
6. Some group leaders cannot handle the pressure; they give whoever makes the most noise most of their attention.
7. Whom did the commission appoint?
8. "In that costume they will never realize who you are!" laughed the duke.
9. I was very excited about meeting Serena Williams, whom I had admired all my life.
10. The young man whom I danced with was an exchange student from Italy. *Or* The young man I danced with was an exchange student from Italy.

Quiz 27-1:   Irregular verbs

Possible revisions:

1. Frustrated that no one responded to my knocking, I rang the doorbell three times.
2. Last weekend Sanya swam the 50-meter backstroke in 32 seconds.
3. Lying on the operating table, I could hear only the beating of my heart.
4. In just a week the ground had frozen, and the first winter storm had left over a foot of snow.
5. Correct

6. When the career counselor gave interviewing tips, Scott clung to her words as if they were gold.
7. The editor explained that the designer had shrunk the image to fit the layout.
8. After seeing her dance in the musical, I would have sworn that she was professionally trained.
9. No matter how much lemonade the budding entrepreneur made, she knew it would be drunk.
10. Correct

Quiz 32-1:   The comma
Possible revisions:

1. As I was finishing an entry in my blog, my supervisor appeared at my office door.
2. The speaker approached the podium with casual, elegant grace.
3. Owning a home, which is a dream for many Americans, seems out of reach when interest rates soar.
4. The study participants began the behavioral therapy and saw immediate results.
5. Correct
6. Cobbled streets too narrow for two cars to pass were lined with tiny houses leaning so close together they almost touched.
7. Correct
8. In one corner of the attic was a box of letters written in the late eighteenth century.
9. Tim O'Brien's third novel, *Going After Cacciato*, won the National Book Award.
10. It has been reported that the Republican who suggested Eisenhower as a presidential candidate meant Milton, not Ike.

Quiz 34-1:   The semicolon and the comma
Possible revisions:

1. The Anglo-American row house achieved its definitive form in seventeenth-century London and was the product of specific social conditions; above all, it was created to meet the needs of an increasingly affluent middle class.
2. Before Chao Neng started his internship, he had no idea how much writing engineers do on the job.
3. It is one thing to be able to read a foreign language with ease; it is quite another to speak it fluently.
4. Correct
5. Many people believe that bats are vicious; in fact, bats are helpful because they eat mosquitoes in large numbers.
6. To my companions, the painting's technique transcended the subject matter; to me it was nothing more than a painting of an old shoe.
7. Culinary experts tend to frown on microwave cooking, which hardens bread and turns the tenderest cuts of meat to rubber.
8. We knew that the river road might be flooded; therefore, we decided to take the longer route through the mountains.
9. Correct
10. The twentieth century saw a bewildering succession of popular dance styles, such as the Charleston, the tango, the jitterbug, the twist, the frug, and break dancing.

Quiz 35-1:   The colon, the semicolon, and the comma
Possible revisions:

1. Ireland has produced an extraordinary number of major literary figures: Oscar Wilde, William Butler Yeats, and James Joyce, to name a few.
2. A flower's reproductive organs consist of the ovary, the style, the stigma, and the stamen.
3. Correct
4. The bomb had torn apart the building and scattered a strange assortment of objects across the street: a television, a dining room set, and several mannequins.
5. Among the classes being offered were Web design, art history, and French.
6. Correct
7. Correct
8. The second and most memorable week of survival school consisted of five stages: orientation, long treks, POW camp, escape and evasion, and return to civilization.
9. Every camper should consider carrying the following items: a first-aid kit, a Swiss army knife, and a flashlight.
10. Hans decided to enrich his life with new cultural activities, such as visiting the modern art museum, taking Chinese lessons, and learning to use a darkroom.

Quiz 62-1:   Identifying nouns

1. Convictions, enemies, truth, lies; 2. Today's (noun/adjective), shocks, tomorrow's (noun/adjective), conventions; 3. words, places, definition, style; 4. man, court, equity, hands; 5. Necessity, mother, invention; 6. family (noun/adjective), system, quarreling, reality, conflict; 7. Advice, injury, medicine, death; 8. children, victims, chaos; 9. iron (noun/adjective), curtain, continent; 10. Frankness, euphemism, rudeness.

Quiz 62-2:   Identifying pronouns

1. One, all; 2. your (pronoun/adjective), you, your (pronoun/adjective), He, you; 3. She, her (pronoun/adjective), nothing, it; 4. Those, who, their (pronoun/adjective); 5. who, anything; 6. me, my (pronoun/adjective), I, it; 7. We, none, us; 8. your (pronoun/adjective), I, you; 9. She, me, that, you; 10. you, it.

Quiz 62-3:   Identifying verbs

1. should be allowed; 2. should, be concentrated; 3. fade; 4. has, been, has been; 5. is; 6. are drowning, [are] starving; 7. will find; 8. Seek, distrust; 9. has annihilated; 10. can, be understood, must be lived.

Quiz 62-4:   Identifying adjectives and adverbs

1. Adjectives: Fat, few; 2. Adjective: irate; adverb: Never; 3. Adjective: spectator; adverb: not; 4. Adjective: disastrous; adverb: equally; 5. Adjectives: small, great; 6. Adjective: unpredictable; adverb: predictably; 7. Adverbs: wisely, cheerfully; 8. Adjective: fashionable; adverb: always; 9. Adjectives: little, proud; adverb: very; 10. Adjectives: your, open; adverb: sufficiently.

Quiz 62-5:   Identifying all parts of speech

1. Adjective: real; adverb: often; 2. Adjective: precious; noun: disagreement; 3. Conjunction: but; verb: has; 4. Noun: stream; preposition: with; 5. Prepositions: from, into; 6. Noun: safety; verb: ferries; 7. Pronoun: you; verb: rust; 8. Adjective: controversial; adverb: inevitably; 9. Adjective: loftiest; verb: rise; 10. Noun: Facts; pronoun: themselves.

Quiz 63-1:   Identifying subjects

1. Complete subjects: Our capacity for justice, our inclination to injustice; simple subjects: capacity, inclination; 2. Complete subject: pockmarks; simple subject: pockmarks; 3. Complete subject: the most deadly poisons; simple subject: poisons; 4. Complete subject: (You); 5. Complete subject: The heresy of one age; simple subject: heresy; 6. Complete subject: A trout in the pot; simple subject: trout; 7. Complete subject: Anger and worry; simple subjects: Anger, worry; 8. Complete subject: The greatest right in the world; simple subject: right; 9. Complete subject: (You); 10. Complete subject: The frog in the well; simple subject: frog.

Quiz 63-2:   Identifying direct objects and subject complements

1. Direct object: the deepest foundations; 2. Subject complement: dangerous; 3. Direct object: his grave; 4. Subject complement: a bucket of ashes; 5. Direct object: the same shoe; 6. Direct object: anything; 7. Subject complement: the only universal language; 8. Subject complement: one of the great arts of conversation; 9. Direct object: hens; 10. Subject complement: drugged and inert.

Quiz 63-3:   Identifying objects and complements

1. Direct objects: liberty, death; indirect object: me, me; 2. Subject complement: graceful; 3. Direct object: one; object complement: warm; 4. Direct object: the future; 5. Subject complements: the songs of despair, the songs of hope; 6. Direct objects: a happy camper, an RV with all the comforts of home; indirect objects: me, you; 7. Direct object: another; 8. Subject complement: unavenged; 9. Direct object: luck; object complement: buttered; 10. Subject complement: the snobbery of the poor.

Quiz 64-1:   Identifying prepositional phrases

1. over a house, on its feet; 2. Without lies, of despair and boredom; 3. of prevailing standards, of our own; 4. with words, with silence; 5. of miscalculations; 6. by a private door, into every individual; 7. In youth, in age; 8. from nothing; 9. in a river, in a graveyard; 10. including this one.

Quiz 64-2:   Identifying subordinate clauses

1. if you stay in a rut; 2. When people are least sure; 3. that the toilet is the seat of the soul; 4. which takes credit for the rain, if its opponents blame it for the drought; 5. what they do not understand; 6. Although ambition by itself is a vice; 7. If you pull out a gray hair; 8. that is given to them; 9. who carves in snow; 10. What is asserted by a man, what is asserted by a woman.

Quiz 64-3:   Identifying verbal phrases

1. Bearing the misfortunes of others; 2. to think wisely, to act foolishly; 3. loaded with gold; 4. To forget one's ancestors, to be a tree without roots; 5. convinced against his will; 6. to see divine light, to put out your own candle; 7. united against a town; 8. defending our prejudices; 9. pervaded from top to bottom by contempt for the law; 10. bearing gifts.

Quiz 65-1:   Identifying sentence types

1. Complex; 2. Compound; 3. Simple; 4. Complex; 5. Compound-complex; 6. Compound; 7. Complex; 8. Simple; 9. Compound-complex; 10. Compound-complex.

ANSWER KEY

Forms A, B, AA, and BB

If you are using the test results to design individualized programs of self-study, the lists on pages 36–37 will show you which sections of *Rules for Writers*, Sixth Edition, the student should turn to. The list on page 36 covers forms A and B, and the list on page 37 covers AA and BB.

1.	C	21.	A	41.	A
2.	C	22.	A	42.	C
3.	D	23.	D	43.	D
4.	D	24.	C	44.	B
5.	C	25.	C	45.	D
6.	B	26.	B	46.	C
7.	C	27.	A	47.	D
8.	B	28.	B	48.	A
9.	C	29.	B	49.	B
10.	C	30.	A	50.	C
11.	B	31.	D	51.	D
12.	C	32.	B	52.	D
13.	B	33.	B	53.	B
14.	A	34.	C	54.	A
15.	C	35.	B	55.	B
16.	C	36.	D	56.	B
17.	A	37.	D	57.	A
18.	C	38.	C	58.	D
19.	C	39.	D	59.	D
20.	B	40.	A	60.	C

Answer Template for Scoring the Diagnostic Tests

FORMS A, B, AA, and BB

PART ONE		PART TWO	

PART ONE

1. A○ B○ C● D○
2. A○ B○ C● D○
3. A○ B○ C○ D●
4. A○ B○ C○ D●
5. A○ B○ C● D○
6. A○ B● C○ D○
7. A○ B○ C● D○
8. A○ B● C○ D○
9. A○ B○ C● D○
10. A○ B○ C● D○
11. A○ B● C○ D○
12. A○ B○ C● D○
13. A○ B● C○ D○
14. A● B○ C○ D○
15. A○ B○ C● D○
16. A○ B○ C● D○
17. A● B○ C○ D○
18. A○ B○ C● D○

19. A○ B○ C● D○
20. A○ B● C○ D○
21. A● B○ C○ D○
22. A● B○ C○ D○
23. A○ B○ C○ D●
24. A○ B○ C● D○
25. A○ B○ C● D○
26. A○ B● C○ D○
27. A● B○ C○ D○
28. A○ B● C○ D○
29. A○ B● C○ D○
30. A● B○ C○ D○
31. A○ B○ C○ D●
32. A○ B● C○ D○
33. A○ B● C○ D○
34. A○ B○ C● D○
35. A○ B● C○ D○

PART TWO

36. A○ B○ C○ D●
37. A○ B○ C○ D●
38. A○ B○ C● D○
39. A○ B○ C○ D●
40. A● B○ C○ D○
41. A● B○ C○ D○
42. A○ B○ C● D○
43. A○ B○ C○ D●
44. A○ B● C○ D○
45. A○ B○ C○ D●
46. A○ B○ C● D○
47. A○ B○ C○ D●
48. A● B○ C○ D○

49. A○ B● C○ D○
50. A○ B○ C● D○
51. A○ B○ C○ D●
52. A○ B○ C○ D●
53. A○ B● C○ D○
54. A● B○ C○ D○
55. A○ B● C○ D○
56. A○ B● C○ D○
57. A● B○ C○ D○
58. A○ B○ C○ D●
59. A○ B○ C○ D●
60. A○ B○ C● D○